# FIVE SESSIONS

# FIVE SESSIONS

# WAR IN THERAPY

## A Novella

by Jaime Estades

Published in 2021 by the
ORI Academic Press, New York, NY

Printed in the United States of America on acid free paper.


**Library of Congress Control Number: 2019943405**


**Cataloging Data:**

Estades, Jaime A. Five Sessions / Jaime A. Estades. Psychohistorical Dialogues Series.

1. Drama. 2. Social Issues – Psychological aspects. 3. Psychohistory. 4. Social history. 5. Analytical sociology. 6. Race relations. 7. Unconscious communications.


**ISBN 978-1-942431-15-2 (soft cover)**

mindmendmedia
piecing it together

Book design, editing, and book cover - by MindMendMedia, Inc. @ MindMendMedia.com

**"Would slaves in the South have felt better about slavery if they had therapy three times a week?"**
**(Super, *Five Sessions*)**

*Five Sessions* was originally twice produced as "workshops" in New York City. The play was experienced by over a thousand people in two different Manhattan theaters, Julia de Burgos in East Harlem and La Tea in the Lower East Side, with sold out audiences at every show. A Q & A session followed each show, with nearly all audience members remaining to participate. The impact among academics and intellectuals, as well as the theater-goers in general, was so significant that Columbia University awarded a grant to its School of Social Work to create a new course based on *Five Sessions*, starting in the fall of 2021. This didactic use of a literary work is cutting edge in the instruction of psychology and policy – within the context of race, oppression, privilege, and power – to impact future therapists.

*To My Daughters*
*Gaby and Jazmin*
*With Love*

# ACKNOWLEDGMENTS

I want to dedicate this book to my two daughters, Gaby and Jazmin, as well as my wife Erika. They acted – from the conception of this play, and then the novel – as my advisors and sounding board for ideas, dialogues, and narrative.

I would like to acknowledge my mother-in-law, Doris (Dodo) Donovan Stern, who helped with editing the novel. I give my sincere thanks to my mother (Margarita Roque), father (Antonio Estades), and my dear brother (Rafael Estades), who are always in my thoughts. My colleagues at Columbia University: Ericka Echevaria, John Robertson, and Ovita Williams. Also, Dorothy Gloster, Eddie Torres, Candido Camacho, and all those who supported the two successful workshop productions of the original play – thank you from the bottom of my heart!

# TABLE OF CONTENTS

## INTRODUCTION TO "FIVE SESSIONS"

"Five Sessions" represents a dialogue between a client and a therapist, where the client asks the therapist a question that no one has so far answered, "Would slaves in the South have felt better about slavery if they had therapy three times a week?" Everyone in the mental health field, psychologists and social workers, take a pause when confronted with this question. And then – there is no answer.

The reality is that the elimination of slavery is the only answer. Today we don't have legalized slavery per se, but we have oppression, racism, classism, and disenfranchisement. Should we include activism as part of therapy when necessary? This novel struggles with that question and others.

It is my belief that today we practice psychotherapy that is beneficial for those who have most of their material needs satisfied, and who have not, historically, experienced discrimination. By contrast, those with ongoing unsatisfied material needs do not respond to such an approach. This therapeutic approach is implemented as a one-size-fits-all, with some minor adjustments here or there. Therefore, why create and/ or use a new psychological, sociological and advocacy approach, when it is more convenient to use the old class white oriented methods? This "bourgeois approach" of American psychology is designed to fit the needs of a specific class, but it is applied to all. I believe in the need to start searching for a new "psychology of the whole," which also embraces the working race, class, and poor who are affected by an economical, sociological, and political pathology that descends upon them as individuals. This is triggered by a long and pervasive history that built this

1

country on class, gender, and race discrimination, which permeates – to this day – all aspects of society.

I believe that one option is to explore the inclusion of macro theories and practices in therapy. When I was in college, I wanted to specialize in industrial psychology in order to help workers with their day-to-day pressures, and improve their working conditions, in conjunction with management. I was immediately disappointed when I found out that industrial psychology's complete orientation was to help the employers extract as much production from the workers as possible, which untimely benefits the management and not the workers.

"Five Sessions" tries to bring up issues that sometimes are not discussed widely, such as those expressed above. It was our experience during the Q & A sessions following seventeen play productions that those who found the play shocking were most likely sitting on top of the cultural totem pole. And those who found it as "extremely needed," because of its "in-your-face disobedience," or even humorous, were most likely sitting at the bottom of the totem pole, showing us how groups react completely differently to the same social and political issues presented to them. Thus demonstrating the great societal divide in which we live.

# STORY

"Five Sessions" is an original play converted into a novella. Synopsis: Current time. "Five Sessions" follows a 24-year-old Caucasian female, a recent Columbia University graduate and therapist, and her very first client, a blue-collar labor leader and suicidal Latino man in his mid-50s, through an agreed-upon five sessions to confront his "issues."

We watch how, through the tensions of race, political correctness, socio-economic differences, and passion, these two characters explore each other's personal struggles and triumphs as they both fight to save his life.

# CAST OF CHARACTERS

**Therapist:** Caroline Kennedy is a recent graduate of Columbia University School of Social Work, Master's level, Catholic 24-year-old woman. She is a white liberal with a good heart who does not easily recognize race and class tension. Her understanding of social and political issues is totally intellectual, and non-experiential. We see her life crumbling – while she works with *"Super"* – due to her relationship with her boyfriend.

*Super*: Vidal Estrella, a dyslexic 58 years old, Latino, building superintendent, and labor leader; he is a college graduate, has an ex-wife and a daughter. He has suffered racial and class discrimination and finds himself face-to-face with a liberal white therapist. Discrimination, combined with his dyslexia, prevented him from finishing law school.

3

These frustrations, truncated dreams, the demeaning treatment towards him by the wealthy tenants whom he serves, and the failure of his marriage have caused him to become suicidal.

**Therapist Supervisor:** A white man in his 40s who supervises the young therapist. He has a lot of experience operating as a social worker in the nonprofit world. He is known for his dark humor.

**Boyfriend:** A hedonistic young white man, Wall Street investment banker, who exhibits his sociopathic behavior through his exertion of control and abuse of people.

**Time:** Present.

## CHAPTER ONE
### *I Am – and That's NOT Enough*

Ever since I was a little girl, I dreamed of becoming the next Joan of Arc for the forgotten. In retrospect, perhaps my desire to be the savior of others was ego driven. Now, I am wallowing in my own frailty and solitude. I wish I could say I was the protagonist of this story, but I can't. How can I be the heroine if I feel like the villain? So, in the end, did I receive what I deserved? I have lost faith not just in my career, but also in myself. I was negligent – oblivious of the world that I actually live in, a world I thought I knew so well.

Today is the anniversary of his death. An event that has kept me in hiding, isolated and afraid of the world for the past year. The memories of that night palpitate in my mind as slowly and irregularly as those of a dying heart. Questions invade me constantly: "Am I responsible for his death? What did I miss? Did I kill him?"

Since I was a child, I wrote in my diary every night. To me, writing a diary was essential. The dairy was my mirror – my secret friend, the sister I never had. When I wrote, I was never lonely or afraid. But a year ago today I stopped writing.

Now, I am a retired therapist after one client, and only five sessions of therapy, that must write again. Otherwise, I'm never going to achieve closure and regain my sanity. I always thought that those who look back the most tend to do so when there isn't much to look forward to. And this is where I am now with only 25 years of existence. Lost.

You may have deduced by now that I am in need of therapy, but I'm far too ashamed to face yet another mental health professional to recount my failures while observing her or his obscured scowls about my incompetence. I admit that sometimes I don't feel entirely miserable. Every now and then, I try to keep myself sane by poking fun at my perception of adversity in my own life. A small dose of satire temporarily does minimize my anxiety and allows me to ridicule my fears.

Now, I'm slowly realizing that there are certain tragic memories that refuse to be postponed. Instead, they haunt me and demand that I confront them.

# CHAPTER TWO

## *My Wealthy Parents*

I've always been drawn to supporting the well-being of others –
at least, that's what I used to tell myself. Gradually this interest formed the
path that led me to major in psychology at Harvard. Thereafter, I
matriculated into the Columbia School of Social Work and graduated with
high honors. Most people would think I was all set, given that I was the
poster child of Ivy League aristocracy, but through this journey I still
managed to become an outcast to my family.

When my parents got married, they were still pretty young and
already on route to disaster. If you ask me, the reason my parents' marriage
failed is clear; they didn't love each other enough to spend a lifetime
together – and even if they did, their love crumbled somewhere down the
line. Now they're just casualties of a futile marriage. It would be tedious
to describe their relationship any further than that. So, I want to speak of
them individually rather than provide some sort of glistening family
portrait.

Each night, my mother, Virginia Morris Adams, would listen to
love songs while clenching her fists. She is a bitter woman with limited
direction and passion. No, actually her singular passion in life is to direct
mine. My mother resented my decision to pursue clinical social work
because she wanted me to take on medicine, even psychiatry, because then
there would be some sort of medical honorific attached to my name and
career. That way, I would be able to cater to the highly privileged and
educated elite that she came from and associates with. She used to criticize

7

me by telling me constantly that 'social workers are the psychologists of poor and uneducated people who are hopeless.'

My mother would then go on to insist that the contribution of our family's foundation was already ample help for 'that element' of society. There was no point in plowing through the lives of the 'sewer-dwellers,' as she would call them, just to make a contribution.

I am the beneficiary of pure old money; my mother inherited her parent's investment banking corporation through a trust – not to mention the multimillion-dollar family foundation. So, to put it simply: Yes, I was brought up pretty well off, more so than most, and still I chose to pursue social work. And that's exactly what we rich folks do, isn't it? Which is whatever the hell we want. Now that I think about it, becoming a clinical social worker might have been some kind of rebellion against my tyrant of a mother. Which might also imply that I would've been better off enrolling in therapy and not in graduate school in the first place.

Let's move on to my father, Charles Adams, who never cared about my future. I can't even recall him ever giving me a piece of advice or even listening to me – whether it was to tell him about my day at school or to alert him that mom was passed out on the kitchen floor from another painkiller overdose. My father apparently listened well when it was important to him to do so, because he managed to become the CEO of one of the largest real estate firms in the tri-state area of New York, New Jersey, and Connecticut.

Perhaps, my main reason for taking on psychology and social work during my years at Harvard and Columbia was so I could one day understand what the hell was wrong with my parents. It's taken a while for me to come to this realization.

## CHAPTER THREE
### *The Hood in the City*

Upon earning my LMSW my goal was to help underserved communities, neighborhoods predominantly inhabited by people of color. I thought I'd finally be fulfilling my lifelong mission of becoming the next Joan of Arc. But looking back that was actually just some bombastic, coded way of harping on my ego, my 'savior complex.' There's no explanation other than that this is pretty much how some rich liberals think when they don't have to consider earning their own money and achieving their own economic stability. Right after my graduation and licensing I was hired as a mental health therapist in a primary care clinic.

While I chose to believe that this was all thanks to my hard-earned degrees coupled with my grit, truthfully it was just some good, old-fashioned nepotism at play. I needn't even provide the details of the interview process; it was boring and – thank goodness – speedy. The job was mine even before I reached out. The clinic had clear favoritism toward Columbia alumni, and they knew exactly what Manhattan family I came from.

Instead of hailing a taxi for that interview, I took the subway for a change, as a good New Yorker should. I hopped on the 1 train toward Port Authority, switched to the shuttle, took the 6th train uptown, and got off at 116th Street and Lexington. I was in East Harlem, stepping on completely new terrain. My friends and I never came to these parts. I'd spent my whole life sheltered away on the West Side, and the East Side of Harlem was another world. We may reside on the same island, but for Westsiders, those on the East Side live entirely separately. We're practically invisible to one another, coexisting like ghosts, or humans, inside haunted houses.

'El Barrio' is what the local folks call it. Westsiders never visit East Harlem. Not everyone can keep up with *El Barrio's* tempo anyway. You see, just about everything in the neighborhood is done with a special kind of rhythm, with almost indescribable electricity. *Tumbao,* as Cuban and Puerto Ricans call one of their *Salsa* rhythms. And while most people wake up to toast, eggs, cereal, and coffee in the morning, *El Barrio* eats *reggaeton*, *salsa*, soul, funk, *ranchera,* rap, and hip-hop for breakfast.

Each day and without fail I could count on these 'dishes' being served red-hot and fresh out on the streets, booming from *bodegas* and food trucks, from neighborhood teenagers hanging out on their stoops, from bustling cars, and even pedestrians tuned into their headphones. If you ever find yourself in *El Barrio*, heritage and culture will gust like an advancing tornado. Navigating oneself required a rhythmic grace that I knew nothing about. I wasn't in Swan Lake anymore; I was in *El Barrio*.

Manhattan is a world, but *El Barrio* is its community. Whether it will remain a community, or rather the same community, I'm not sure. Remember when I mentioned that people don't visit *El Barrio*? Well, it's true. Instead, they come in and make themselves right at home. There's been a swarming influx of yuppies moving in and robbing *El Barrio* of that vibrant personality that draws people like me. Basically, when they move in, the rent goes up, and black and brown folks get kicked out. Yuppies are even saying 'Spa-Ha' now, as a diminutive for Spanish Harlem. But what do I know? I'm probably just as white and just as privileged as the next yuppie, so I'm not so off the hook either.

CHAPTER THREE

I will say, though, that I do love how the word *Barrio* just clicks and glides off the tongue, leaving the mouth with a tender flick. Sure, 'Spa-Ha' might sound easier, especially to white Anglophonic ears, but *Barrio* is without a doubt a much better word to capture the essence of a community in all its Latin and Caribbean flare. So maybe this yuppie does know a thing or two after all.

I learned that East Harlem has the second-largest concentration of public housing in the United States, just after Brownsville in Brooklyn. In addition to staggering poverty rates, the neighborhood also exhibits the highest unemployment rate of the entire city. A stroll through East Harlem can sometimes feel like walking through an abandoned hospital, passing limbless casualties of diabetes, asthma, substance abuse, AIDS, and various other diseases. And even though the average rate of East Harlem residents with mental illnesses appears to be parallel to the rest of New York City, access to treatment for them is much more limited. So, there I was, little Ms. Joan of Arc to the rescue, stationed on the second floor of a nonprofit primary care center in one of the poorest neighborhoods in the United States.

Something that I learned very quickly regarding Latinos, and especially Puerto Ricans, is that in El Barrio politics is not like a sporadic rain that passes by as a topic of discussion. It's more like a national sport. *El Barrio* inhabitants' cultural DNA is made of chemical political brain combinations not yet discovered, and not represented on the periodic table of elements. Sorry for that stereotype, but I think they would agree with me proudly.

If you go to East Harlem, you can hear residents talking as if they were the street's Socrates, Plato, and Aristotle discussing the virtues and decadence of contemporary politics. They dissect every topic in the same way as "Don Moncho", the butcher who had a butcher shop next to the primary clinic. He dissected politics just as he dissected pigs with his machete.

Latinos can't have a good day if they don't criticize elected officials, policies, and world tensions. There is no ambiguity regarding their conclusions either. If you misstate anything, you're 'totally' wrong – not 'actually' wrong or 'somewhat' wrong – you are 'totally' wrong. Therefore, you are a liar, or you don't know what you are talking about. Someone wins, so someone has to lose. That's the sport.

# CHAPTER FOUR
## *The Job!*

The director was a 60-year-old psychiatrist named Joe Katz. Lanky and sickly-looking, his demeanor was harsh and cynical, calloused by spending about thirty-five years at the only workplace he'd ever known.

Psychiatrists are MDs with a couple of semesters of psychology under their belts. That permits them to prescribe medications like any other M.D. And that's what made my mother such a loyal client and supporter of Joe's. She received all the painkillers she could ask for.

Psychologists and clinical social workers, on the other hand, cannot prescribe medications. They focus exclusively on the patient's emotional and mental state through psychotherapy, which my mother probably could have benefitted from. Joe was pretty much my mother's drug dealer – or 'pusher – with license' as they would say in *El Barrio*. Apparently, it was even an ongoing joke within the staff to call him 'Joe Amazon'. Whenever my mother needed her painkillers, all she had to do was place an order through Joe's secretary.

No one benefited more from that board funding through her foundation's grants, my mother had helped Joe for years to keep his non-profit organization financially afloat. In its storied past the foundation had a lot of formal requirements that needed to be satisfied before any funds to nonprofit organizations were approved. Now that my mother was in charge, the main criterion was an unwritten one that was created by my mother. It was this: 'whomever the fuck my mother wanted to give the

15

money to.' That was it. The board was there for the great food during the monthly board meetings, and for the board retreats in fancy hotels in the Caribbean and Las Vegas.

The following week I was waiting to meet with Joe and to meet my first client. I had never worked for a salary. I was feeling so proud that I was making my own money for the first time ever, and about to engage with the world as a professional therapist.

The receptionist gave me three intake assessments for potential clients. One of the cases got my attention more than the other two: a Latino superintendent of a building on the Upper East Side. His name was Vidal Estrella. His file stated that he had attempted suicide three times, but didn't specify how. I thought it understandable that he didn't want to elaborate about the attempted suicides during the intake session.

His employer wanted him fired, but his union intervened in his favor. Eventually the union and the condo board chair agreed to allow him to continue working as long as he attended therapy. Unfortunately, his union health care insurance was limited to only five sessions.

I learned later that the people in the neighborhood called him 'Super.' I also learned that he did not fit the stereotype of a typical building superintendent. My potential client had a long history of union, political, and community activism.

Another thing I learned in my first week at the program was that there is no confidentiality of cases whatsoever. Everybody knows everybody. Most people knew or had heard 'Super stories' in the community, unless they came to work in the neighborhood from outside like me.

*Super* supervised an assistant who stayed overnight in the building while *Super* kept his own apartment in *El Barrio.* The cause was that he wanted to continue to do his political work in the community. There were also some other reasons that he wanted to live that way, which I didn't know about until much later. Apparently, he requested to be seen by a therapist in East Harlem, near his home, but in complete secrecy. His reasons were twofold. First, his hours were already irregular due to his volunteer activism and he didn't want to be late to work. Second, he also had an occasional part-time evening job as a waiter for a catering service.

According to the file, *Super* didn't want anyone from the neighborhood to know that he was attending the mental health clinic. As part of the deal with his union, *Super* was to be registered as a medical patient in the primary care section of the clinic. He would be contacted by the therapist through that primary care section to avoid rumors of his suicide attempts floating around to the many people who knew him in the neighborhood.

The intake social worker saw me in the hallway reading the intake report on *Super*. She stopped to talk to me about the case. She said that she didn't know him personally, but she had heard of *Super* as a well-known political activist in the Latino and minority communities in New York City during the 1970's, especially in East Harlem. He was known as a fiery defender of economic rights: fighting against discrimination and racism in the state and city governments and corporations, corrupt and racist politicians, and gentrification.

Also, she had heard that *Super* was a self-declared socialist. Then I remembered this politician who was running for President – Bernie

Sanders – who had ideas on how to help poor and working people. I remembered that he had described himself as a socialist. I don't follow politics at all, but I watch the news once in a while, and I had heard about Mr. Sanders. But I didn't know much about socialism. I had heard about socialism a couple of times before Mr. Sanders. I knew it had to do with Russia, the Russian satellite countries, and a Cold War with the Russian block that took place a long time ago. I also knew that my parents hated the word 'socialism.' Now that I know more about it, I think that my mother acts like a socialist since she runs a charitable foundation that grants funds largely to nonprofits that serve the poor. But, if I suggested that to her, she might take more pills than she is used to and fatally overdose.

I asked myself, 'What type of therapy do you use to treat a socialist?' I had never even had a real conversation with a political activist in my life, not to mention a socialist. The word socialist was a distant word within my vernacular. If anything, I associated it with radical ideas and troublemakers.

Anyway, I kept finding this case more fascinating than the other two cases. Those cases dealt mostly with schizophrenia and depended – according to their records – on medication prescribed by Joe, who saw them regularly. *Super,* even when suicidal, was not psychotic. He had not broken with reality, or heard voices, or had delusions. It seemed that he was very much aware of his suicidal condition. Still, based on the preliminary intake assessment, I believed that he suffered from anxiety and depression.

*Super* also had a strong philosophical belief in existentialism. I had vaguely learned about that in an introductory course on philosophy at Harvard, but therapy for believers in existentialism was not taught to students at Columbia. Many existentialists are atheist or agnostic. They are often perceived as having a very pessimistic view of life when they opine that life itself has no purpose, and that humans often just go through the motions. Trying to make sense of a life without a God, without a compass to define good and evil, and with no mystical beliefs of reward and punishment leads the individual to being interpreted by many therapists as depressive.

I definitely wanted to know more about him. Curiosity kept flirting with me. However, at that point, I had no idea who would be my first client, so I brushed those desires aside and waited for my first case to be officially assigned. Even when I had read all the potential cases in the hallway, little did I know what was coming into my life. Then the secretary told me to meet the director in my new office down the hall. He was waiting to introduce me to my first case.

## CHAPTER FIVE

### *My Mother and Joe*

Ironically, my mother is very protective of me now that I'm an adult. She tries to modify my life more than a fucking adverb. I think she overprotects me to compensate for sending me to boarding school when I was 12 years old. That was at the insistence of my father, who I don't think felt comfortable with children trying to get his attention while he was doing absolutely nothing at home.

After my graduation as a clinical therapist, I had told my mother, in passing, that I wanted to work in a similar organization to Joe's. Just to be clear – I didn't declare, 'I want to work for Joe.' I had good academic credentials and could have been hired anywhere, but I really wanted to work with 'challenged communities' as some people in the profession are used to calling them. Now, after a whole year, I still remember what *Super* told me once that the so-called 'challenged communities' are not the hoods, but the federal, state, and city governments.

My mother, knowing that I always get what I want, thought that the best way to keep an eye on me, as if I were still a baby, was for me to work for Joe. She didn't tell me that she had told Joe to give me the job right after my graduation from Columbia. But I knew she did. My mother – besides being addicted to pills – is not translucent like Norway's northern lights. Rather, she is entirely transparent.

## CHAPTER SIX

### *The First Session: What Did I Get Into?*

As you can guess, Joe was more than happy to please my mother in anything she wanted. And happy Joe was – for obvious reasons – employing me. Not only did he get to hire me with my great credentials and recommendations, but he also got to please my mother's foundation.

When I arrived in front of my new office, I heard Joe's voice through the door talking on the telephone. I decided not to enter since I didn't want to interrupt. However, I was able to hear the conversation. Immediately, I realized that he was talking to my mother. Suddenly, I felt the confidence I had been developing for more than 24 years diminish right then and there, as I realized that I was a clinical therapist with a master's degree from an Ivy League school still being protected by her mom.

I remembered that I had mentioned in passing to my mother that I wanted to start with challenging cases and not be '*baby-sat.*' But my mother couldn't help herself and told Joe that I had already worked with a couple of challenging cases through Columbia internships, and that I felt prepared. I never asked her to advocate for me with Joe, and I never asked her to get me a job in his organization.

I learned by 'unintentionally' listening to Joe with my right ear to the door that she wanted me to keep my mind occupied with work rather than thinking about my boyfriend and his family, whom she hated.

"Virginia! Thank you for calling me back. I just wanted to tell you how happy I am to have your daughter working here as a therapist. What? You want me to give her that case we talked about? So she can keep her mind off her boyfriend. – Yeah, Yeah – Oh. – That's idiotic! – What! – NO! I didn't mean to suggest that your daughter is an idiot. – Yes, that's what I meant. – He is the idiot. – Right. – This is a tough case, Virginia. She is not ready. Nobody starts a career in therapy with such a case. I mentioned that case to you for funding purposes only. – Of course, we need your foundation support. – I know that Virginia. – Listen, I gave her a couple of cases to read as well as that case. – Ok. I will give her the case when she gets here. – You're welcome." I heard the hard click of him putting the phone down, and then, "Dammit!"

As you can see, my mother is as persistent as time. There she was on my first day of work, once again meddling in my business, including talking about my boyfriend. I was embarrassed that my mother took such liberty. Not to mention that now it seemed that (according to her and Joe) I was ill prepared and not ready to take on a challenging case. I wasn't ready? Then what the hell were the last 6 years of theory, internships, and training at two of the most prominent Ivy League universities in the country like Harvard and Columbia worth?

Then Joe opened the door and said, "Hey! You are early! I like that. Please come in. How are you?"

"Great! It's nice to see you again. Mom sends her regards."

"You know, everybody loves your mother in this City. Please, sit."

"Thanks."

"We already hung your diploma and certificate right there. He pointed to the wall and asked, "Nervous?"

"Excited!" I said.

"Excited? What are you excited about? You're a clinical therapist."

"I don't want to be rude, but you hired me because of my credentials, not because of my mother. You know that she likes to meddle a lot."

"Tell me about it! Listen, I heard you were at the top of the class at Columbia. However, I also heard from one of your professors that you are a bit unconventional. So, I have to warn you. You can't use your gut here. Okay?"

"Of course. I mean… No problem."

As you can see, it seems that I had a reputation, and perhaps a negative one, among some of my professors at Columbia for following my instincts and doing things out of the ordinary during my internship. That was permissible once in a while as long as it didn't deviate too much from the therapeutic plan. However, it seems that my reputation had caught up with me.

Joe said, "We are going to start you with only one case. However, this case is a challenging one. I will be supervising you very closely. His name is Vidal Estrella, but people call him *Super*."

"Bingo! The case I wanted," I said to myself. However, I had noticed the great cultural difference between my client and me, so I decided to test Joe a little. I said, "I read his file, and I have a question. You said during my job interview that you try to match therapists and clients according to their cultural backgrounds to ease the connection. Why did you give me this case?"

Joe responded, "Two words: Non-Profit. We don't have enough clinical social workers. We can't do cultural matches all the time. The budget and politics influence practice. Another thing, his insurance pays for only five sessions. Just a warning! We learned a week ago during intake that he has no problem in speaking his mind. We will have supervision once a week, and whenever you need me. I'm going to get him now. Good luck."

Joe didn't have enough clinical social workers, but the real truth was that my mother convinced him to give me a tough case to keep my mind off my boyfriend. She also knew that I wanted to start my career with a tough case in order to prove myself.

Between that instant and the moment I met *Super,* each second felt like an hour. Finally, my first case came into the office and stood right at the door and looked straight into my eyes in a very serious and confident manner. He seemed to be asking himself, 'What am I doing here with this kid in this room?' I didn't blame him if that was what he was thinking. I was 24 years of age, and he was 60.

Then he stopped looking at me and began looking around the room. He saw a small shelf of books on top of a table on the left side of the door. He grabbed one book and flipped a couple of pages, stared at it briefly, and then put it back on the shelf. Right then and there I knew that he was really educated, not because he grabbed a book, but because I could tell that he knew how to hold books as if he owned them.

I was impressed by his deep exotic brown skin, and a stare like an ancient Mongol warrior, looking at me and the room as if he was in command of the situation. His long gray hair had not experienced the sensations of a hairbrush plowing through it in days. He was taller than me, but who isn't? I have to admit that I felt nervous for the first time. White people don't look like that. Am I wrong to say that?

I had all those thoughts in the few seconds that we had staring at each other. He had deep beautiful black eyes and wide shoulders. He was so charismatic that there was even a vibrant musical tone in his breathing. I was trying to guess his personality before we talked, even though I knew that was considered a big mistake before you started your first session, but my brain froze as it devoured these first impressions. I ended up saying the only 'safe word' that all humans use to break the ice when they are nervous, "Hi!"

"OK," he responded.

"Please sit." I said, but he didn't sit. He kept staring at me. I said to myself, "What is this about? This is not what I practiced at Columbia. He is supposed to sit."

I was trained to not initiate the conversation on any topic until the client initiates the conversation, because 'the sessions are about the client and not the therapist.' This forces the client to speak first. Therefore, I waited for him to say something. No verbalization came from him, so there was a long silence between us as we stared at each other. As I waited, my brain was telling me how dumb this strategy was.

And then *Super* spoke, "Are you waiting for me to say something?"

"He got me," I thought to myself. He knows my strategy. I panicked a little more. It's one thing to be at school protected by your teachers, and another thing being on your own. It's like going from the lab studying the genetics of a lion to finding yourself in the jungle with the lion. That's when your instincts dominate your strategies more than your supposedly educated and disciplined brain. I said, "Well, if you want to share your thoughts that would be great."

"My thoughts? Regarding?"

"About anything you want to talk about."

"You want to hear my thoughts?"

"Yes."

"Why?"

"I would love to hear what is on your mind, but only if you want to share."

He responded, "Why don't you share your thoughts with me? Of course, that is, if you want to share."

I thought to myself, "He is not following the script, where he tells me his problem, and I advise, and we take it from there."
Then the response came like lighting, "OK. Since it's up to me then, tell me about yourself."

What? – What was that? This is not about me. I'm the therapist. After a long pause, my instincts took over brilliantly, I thought, and I said, "Again, this is about you, not me." "Shit!" I thought to myself, "That wasn't brilliant at all."

He said, "You just said that I could develop the conversation anyway I want to. Well, tell me about you."

"Yes, I said that, but if it were about me, then you wouldn't benefit from these sessions."

"Then why didn't you say that at the beginning instead of remaining quiet? We have already wasted time talking about you and your rules instead of me. Does this make sense to you? Why didn't you just say, 'Please, start by telling me something about yourself'?"

After this lecture on what my work should be, these were my thoughts: First, 'What should I say now?' Second, 'I'm so stupid.' Third, 'I should have gone to law school.' Fourth, 'The tactic of remaining in silence waiting for the client to speak may work better with the upper middle class, but certainly not with non-white cultures, and communities of color, or poor people.'

I know now that people in each culture introduce themselves differently. Some are more passive, more respectful and ritualistic, while others are more assertive. I remember that a black student at Columbia looked as if she couldn't stand the school because she was always demonstrating to all the white students how privileged they were. One day she announced in class – in what the students thought was a political diatribe and embarrassed the professor – that she was changing her major because she thought that the psychology being taught at the school had nothing to do with the poor and people of color. She called the psychology that we were learning a *'bourgeoisie psychology'* that only worked for people who had their material needs satisfied: not for the poor, working people, and people of color. I didn't understand her at that time, but *Super* definitely sounded like her. Perhaps she was right because this shit wasn't working for me, and I doubt that it was working for him. But it was still early in our relationship. So, I said, "OK, that's fair. Tell me your thoughts about being here."

"You're a Columbia girl. Aren't you"?

I was shocked. How does he know that I went to Columbia University?

"Pardon me?"

"You went to Columbia University." He said it as a statement of fact.

"How do you know I studied at Columbia?"

"Look, *Columbia*, you put the diploma right behind your head like a crown so we pitiful people know how much more educated than us you are."

"What?"

"Look behind you, *Columbia*!" Joe had instructed his assistant to hang it on the wall behind my desk, and I had not noticed it yet.

"Oh! I forgot! Silly me. If you don't mind, please don't call me '*Columbia*'! By the way, I was at the top of my class."

There was my second mistake in less than 5 minutes. How arrogant, defensive, and insecure I felt after I said that 'I was at the top of my class.' Not only that, I gave him potential ammunition to make this conversation more about me than about him.

And there he went, "Top of your class, ah? Good to know… Good to know."

I knew then that I had to change strategies and be more direct.

"I didn't mean it that way. Anyway, let's start again. Why are you here?"

"SUICIDE!"

I knew it. It was in the record, and still it surprised me when he said it. However, my training kicked in. The trick is to encourage the conversation when you have no fucking idea what to say next. Therefore, you may end up saying something stupid and condescending like, "That's a good start."

And then after thinking how stupid that also sounded, I started talking about potential symptoms regarding depression and suicide. "Let me ask you. Do you feel tired? A lack of energy? Depressed?" And then he changed the subject by taking me deep into a huge dialectal ocean. I realized then that Columbia Social Work School should have had a course especially on how to treat clients who are sharper, better read, and smarter than you.

He said, "Faulkner, you know, Faulkner. You were top of the class at Columbia. You must have read him. He wrote, 'They killed us, but they didn't whip us yet.' I bet you have heard about the Masada Jews too. They preferred to kill themselves and their children than to give the Romans the pleasure of whipping them. In New York, the buildings are mountains! Show me one poor building, and I will show you a mountain being surrounded. Listen, *Columbia*, wealthy people die from depression. Poor people die from anger!"

All I could say was, "That's interesting…"

He immediately interrupted me, "Interesting? Listen, a month ago, a single mother lost her cleaning job and her apartment. She ended up in a crowded shelter while ACS tried to take her baby away. Two days ago, she killed herself and the baby. She was angry. What's the treatment for that? Do you think that slaves in the South would have felt better about slavery if they had therapy three times a week?"

The sociological and psychological theories that were taught to me – each separately, and suddenly, merged on that slavery question. It took a building superintendent to teach me that complexity after thousands of dollars spent on Ivy League educations. Still, I couldn't answer the question, nor could I admit that he was ahead of me, so all I could say was, "I don't see the connection."

He repeated, "Would slaves have felt better about slavery if they would have had therapy three times a week? Please answer me *Columbia*."

He knew he had put me against the wall, and he was not going to let go of me. Therefore, I had to surrender for the sake of the session. I had to be honest, while deflecting a little bit of his use of '*Columbia*.' That was already getting on my nerves. I said, "I see your point, but please don't call me '*Columbia*.'"

"What's your name, then?" he replied.

"Oh, I'm sorry, so rude of me. Christine Adams. And your name is Vidal Estrella. But you like to be called *Super*, or so I gather from your intake record. – I need to know something. Do you still want to commit suicide?"

He replied, "Should therapists use the word suicide?"

I said to myself, "Fuck me, here we go again."

"Anyway, you can use it with me," he continued. "Listen, I don't want to kill myself. I want to die. I already feel dead. Let me ask you; when you are a ghost, how do you commit suicide?"

# CHAPTER SIX

The truth is that I didn't know if I could use that word or not since I never had a suicide case in my internship, and the little that I knew about suicides didn't cover whether using the word 'suicide' was appropriate for me during the session.

This also made me wonder if he had been to therapy before, even though he had stated during intake that he had never been to therapy. He seemed to know a lot for a first-time user of therapy. At any rate, I determined that I wouldn't use that word again unless he brought it up. Well, at least I was going to try. For some reason, I felt that I was gaining confidence. I was finally entering into a flow.

So, I responded, "Obviously I'm not a ghost. Therefore, I'm not qualified to answer that question. – Now, let me ask you, is the desire more prevalent now?"

"Like you, I'm living this life to die. We are all carrying a coffin on our backs."

"You should give yourself credit. Sixty years of perseverance, of living. There must be some happy moments somewhere in those years. – Don't you think?"

"I have been walking day and night with my head down for sixty years, staring at the street hoping to find one piece of pavement that can cheer me up. Can you see me breathing?"

"Yes."

"Well, that's failure! I see news of people committing suicide and I'm impressed with their courage. Society calls them cowards, but to me they are heroes."

"Why are they heroes?"

"They are the ultimate rebels; they rebel against God! They tell God to fuck off! This life is mine! Not God's."

"Do you believe in God?"

"Agnostic, which means, who the fuck knows!? If God exists, religions are God's headaches. They give God a bad reputation. If God exists, he could be in therapy! – I am also an existentialist."

"Can you explain the difference between agnosticism and existentialism?"

"The agnostic says, 'Who the fuck knows if God exists or not,' and an existentialist doesn't give a shit if God exists. My life belongs to me, not God."

I answered, "Perhaps."

He raised his eyebrows and said, "Perhaps? Why perhaps?"

"Maybe I'm agnostic." I said with a little smile. He didn't smile back. I continued, "You also said that religions give God a bad reputation?"

"When you pretend to have the monopoly on the truth about something, that's religion! But who the fuck knows? – You see?"

He smiled, and I pretended. He went from combining psychology and sociology, to metaphysics and theology in less than 15 minutes. I was not getting specific, but I was learning much about how he sees himself and the world even when he wasn't talking about why he wanted to commit suicide. I knew that it was still early in therapy, and he needed to trust me more before feeling comfortable and opening up.

However, my inner voice, which I now call 'my inexperience,' was demanding that I get to the point immediately, even though I found

34

him fascinating. He was taking me to areas that I had never questioned before, but I had to control my focus. I needed to be patient, which is not one of my strongest attributes.

Then I remembered the advice that a professor gave me regarding specificity and shorthand language with your clients. She said, "Listen, clients are not office memos that tell you exactly what your boss wants you to do." I took a deep breath and exhaled all my nervousness into the room. It was so obvious that I think he saw it floating around in the air.

I asked, "Have you ever thought of anything that might prevent you from ending your life?"

"Well, what if God exists, and suicide is considered a request for divine asylum in heaven, and I end up detained in limbo without a hearing. …Well, that would be a deterrent for me. Don't you think?"

I never saw suicide as illegal immigration. I asked, "What would you say to God, if He had asked about your suicide?"

"Nothing."

"Why?"

"*Columbia*, don't think for a second that because you're a therapist, you are God in this office."

"I wouldn't presume. …Believe me, I wouldn't presume."

"This is not a comfortable chair. I have a bad back. Do you mind if I stand?

"No, if it makes you feel comfortable. I will ask the director for a new one." One of the things I noticed immediately about working in nonprofits located in poor neighborhoods is that their budgets are not enough to pay for a decent chair, computer, or desk. My chair, as well as his, felt like a toilet seat, or like sitting on the hole of a donut. Regardless of those material realities, one of the few things I knew about people with suicidal tendencies is that for the most part they create a plan to commit suicide. They may even elaborate it over a long time. And the reason I wanted to attack the issue right away was because I had no idea at what crisis level he was operating at that moment. I didn't want to take any risks. Therefore, I needed to start to decipher whether this suicidal client was close to attempting suicide or not as soon as possible. I needed to listen more. So far, I was on the periphery of his thoughts. I had to push a bit more. "Let me ask you how you see your existence in the after-life without a God?"

*Super* was already standing, pacing around the room with his back toward me. Suddenly he turned, looking straight at me. "Oh! That's a smart question. Good! If I am suicidal, I may have questioned where I would end up. – Talking about God. Isn't that an expensive crucifix on your neck? – Catholic? – Ah!"

I meant to take my crucifix off that morning, but I forgot. He found another excuse to potentially sabotage the session and to avoid talking about his needs. It is important that the therapist's office and physical presentation look as neutral as possible in order to avoid unnecessary distractions and misinterpretations of your intentions. You and your surroundings must look as objective and neutral as possible

So, I admitted, "You are right, I forgot. I shouldn't have. – Yes. I'm a Catholic.

He then pointed at my crucifix and said, "Since you brought it up. Let's talk about Christianity."

"No, I didn't bring it up."

"You bring it up when you wear that crucifix to work. You know that, *Columbia*."

"Jesus Christ!" I said, frustrated

"He's exactly the one I want to talk about. The Bible says that Jesus went to Jerusalem with the single purpose of getting killed. Well, that sounds like fucking suicide to me. – And you have the nerve to advise me while wearing a crucifix. Who do you think needs therapy – you or me? And here I am, listening to a fucking Catholic, of all fucking people. Isn't that ironic?! Listen, *Columbia*, suicide is the ultimate act of freedom. If we had been born with a switch to kill ourselves, nobody would be here."

"Perhaps, we weren't given a switch so that we had to overcome challenges and make progress. Maybe that's the reason we don't have a switch to die, so that we can give ourselves an opportunity to grow... Don't you think?"

"*Columbia*, I'm sixty! Sixty! There is not one question about life and death that you can ask me that I haven't asked myself already. You are a kid, *Columbia*. You can't help me."

"I'm not *Columbia*! My questions are just..."

"The questions are yours; the answers are mine, *Columbia*."

"Do you have as high standards for others as you do for yourself?" I said.

He responded, "I always find people with high self defense mechanisms to be extremely deceiving individuals."

I thought that we were finally in my territory. "Yes, if the therapy was about me. – You seem to know about defense mechanisms."

"I know a bit about Freud. I went to college, and law school for a while."

"Why didn't you finish law school?"

"I was married with a baby. It was either paying for the baby or paying for the law books… The baby was cheaper and better looking."

"Finally," I thought to myself, "he volunteered something." I took a breath and thought, "If he left law school because of the baby, then he loves the baby very much!"

I asked him, "So, what things upset you the most?"

"Listen, I'm just tired and pissed, like most people."

"But not everyone who is frustrated is thinking of ending his or her life."

"What city are you living in? Even bankers are killing themselves."

"Why do you feel so certain of that?"

"Do you think New York City is a romantic movie? Oh, I'm sorry. I forgot. You're a rich white girl from Columbia University."

Something was clear. He knew how different we were regarding our class and race. Calling me 'Columbia' illuminated those realities for him. However, it was getting on my nerves. I said, "We can have a civil conversation. Let's try not to make it personal."

"You're asking me about my life, and you don't want to make it personal? Who trained you? Oh! I forgot, a bunch of white teachers at Columbia University."

# CHAPTER SIX

"You seem to be tough on whites in academia?"

"It's a demographic fact about Ivy League education. Faculties are disproportionately white, as well as the students."

"I was just describing…," I started to say when he cut me off.

"You don't approve because your political correctness says that racism applies to white folks too, so it seems that now I'm the racist one."

"Well, that's not what I meant."

"NO! NO! Hold on. We need to realize something here. We are both humans, but we are situated differently. Can we acknowledge that? Answer me! Can we acknowledge at least that?"

"Of course, please make your point. I'm listening."

And he did. Oh my God did he let me have it! And, I never heard the following argument before. I thought that even when society is not perfect, it was good enough for everybody, and pretty much equal. Boy, was I wrong. So, he continued, "People like you use political correctness to medicate your white guilt and impose your PC on us like we are the fucked-up ones! Like you know better what the words oppression, discrimination, 'spic,' and 'nigger' mean, and we don't. Listen! The biggest poverty pimps are white-run nonprofits like this one; taking lots of foundation money while making you look like you give a shit. *Columbia*, our communication would be more honest and productive if you felt more awareness than guilt. Guilt is a big cross to carry." He stared at my crucifix, his face serious and contemplative, and finished, "Don't you think?"

I have learned since those five sessions that many non- profit agencies operating in poor neighborhoods have boards with a significant number of white members in order to raise enough money for the organization. Unfortunately, the affluent whites end up exerting a great influence on how the organizations are run, including hiring staff that looks mostly like them, especially in the executive positions. *Super* wasn't wrong. I had no other choice but to accept his political opinion. So, I said, "I didn't mean to insert political correctness into the conversation."

"I'm sorry if I'm too blunt, but I'm too old to pretend! You can afford to pretend. Not me."

"Again," said I, trying to sound patient, "these sessions are about you, please don't make this about me."

His response was sharp and fast. "This isn't worthy! At least it isn't if we don't talk about the things that bother me, and instead talk about what makes you comfortable."

Then I said, "Of course, we can talk about what bothers you. Tell me more about it."

"My point is that suicide should be an option on the menu of every rational person. You don't get a good taste of life until you hate yourself."

And when everything seemed that it was going back to normal, I spoke again with my foot in my mouth. – Triggering another excuse not to deal with the issue.

"Are you saying that self-hate is pleasurable?"

"Now I want God to exist! So he can take me out of this fucking room! – If you don't feel guilty about things that you have done in life, then you haven't embraced life. Do you want to try?"

"Try what?"

"Self-hate, *Columbia*!"

By that time, I was really tired of him calling me 'Columbia', and treating me like a kid. Not only that, but I had also lost total control by letting my frustrations take control of me, something that rarely happened.

"Well, you have done a good job at trying to make me hate myself. For some reason you have assumed that I'm a privileged white person."

"Well, you've had it coming for a couple of centuries. What will you tell death when it comes to get you, Columbia?"

"Well, death may have the wrong person, since my name is not 'Columbia'!"

"Death knows who you are. And – don't get upset – it seems that you may be in need of therapy."

I was getting upset now. "I am not upset. It's just that this is not about me. It's about you. Let's continue. Shall we?"

"Let's 'shall'," he said with enthusiasm.

I was embarrassed about my reaction. I was still angry with him, but mostly with myself. I was a mess. I needed to change the subject to his suicide immediately.

"How do you feel about your life? Just in general."

"I told you. Dead! Sometimes we die breathing, walking with our eyes open. I'm trying to find a place where the universe can't find me."

"But you are still performing, working, living. You are alive."

"I'm full of shit. I'm a coward. I haven't done it yet."

"How many times have you attempted?"

"Three times. Once at work, and the second time at the union hall. I fainted on both occasions."

"Do you remember how you felt before you fainted those two times?"

"As I said, you are angry and tired of not making sense of life. Then, you realize that you have been staring at a wall for a long time for no reason, feeling your body shrinking while everything around you gets bigger and denser and denser, like a black hole trying to suck you up. The walls get closer, trying to squeeze you. The pressure in your chest is so much that you can't breathe, but the suffocation doesn't kill you. You feel that you are going to gasp for air for eternity. Then, you faint, waking up later next to an open window surrounded by people. I woke up disappointed that I couldn't do it."

"Unfortunately," I said, "time is up. Let's continue on this topic next time. Listen, you mentioned that you attempted to end your life three times. Next time. I want you to tell me about the third time. Okay?"

"Listen carefully, my insurance can pay for only five sessions. We already wasted one day. I'm trying hard, very hard. You have four more sessions left. You need to do a lot better than today."

"I will see if I can persuade the insurance to give you more sessions."

"Persuade a bureaucracy? How can you persuade something that has no soul? Four more sessions – and get me a better chair next time! I didn't come here to be tortured." He couldn't help himself from letting me know how naïve I was one more time. He walked out slamming the door behind him.

# CHAPTER SEVEN
## *My Boyfriend*

Let me go straight to the point here, because I really can't spend too much time writing about this chapter in my life. But first, women are keyboards for men to write their own stories. When we fall in love, love becomes a voluntary blindness. I learned something from this relationship. Don't put on your eyeglasses if you are going to keep your eyes closed. That summarizes for me the relationship with my former boyfriend.

I met Michael Waldman in my Catholic *Opus Dei* type of co-ed boarding school in Vermont, when I transitioned from the junior high division to the high school. Michael is the most handsome man that I have ever met in my life.

He was born to one of the richest families in New York City. His parents own the majority of stocks in the one of the biggest investment banks in the world. I saw him at parties and school gatherings. He is three years older than me. We spoke once in a while. Not all the girls in the school were in love with him as I was. Some of those girls were smarter about love than me. Some of them found him arrogant and presumptuous. I had the same thoughts on some occasions, but when I was talking to him, none of that registered with me.

We never had sex during my boarding school years, not even a kiss, since the competition was overwhelming. Also, I was 3 years younger, and I didn't think he would be interested sexually in someone so much younger. I was extremely shy around him. Even though I thought myself pretty enough, I didn't find myself interesting enough to hold

43

Michael's attention. Another reason that I chose to study psychology. But don't get the wrong idea, I generally was a pretty confident adolescent.

Most of the girls in the school were competing to see who could entice him first, but he was so popular that it was difficult to get a date with him – not to mention that in our boarding school setting a girl had to wait until the weekend before she could bump into him in town. Michael had a reputation among his former lovers for not using condoms while having sex, because he wanted 'to have the full sexual experience.' Because, after all, you know, sex was about him. As you can see, the Catholic school didn't have much influence on him or the girls who pursued him constantly. Anyway, at the end of the day, sex always beats religion.

There were rumors about two girls having abortions after having sex with Michael. It wasn't only Michael's self-indulgence, but also that some of the girls were stupid enough not to use contraceptives. Maybe it was the failure of the school's abstinence teachings, joined with Michael's idiocy, that got them pregnant.

My Catholicism was not fanatical in any way, shape, or form, but I was always very religious. I attended Catholic schools from kindergarten to my senior year at the boarding school. I was one of those girls that believed everything that was taught in school without questioning. Therefore, Catholicism is still a big part of me.

I still go to church on Sundays, but that doesn't mean that I don't have desires like any other woman – at least that's what I thought. Religion is at least a good emergency brake to avoid sexual accidents. I thought of it as a moral contraceptive. Additionally, I had a deep apprehension that I would not be good in bed. In short, I was a virgin until my last year at Harvard.

I went to St. Patrick Cathedral on the second Easter after I returned to New York, to work on my Master's degree at Columbia. I saw Michael after seven years. As the priest preached about the importance and joy of the resurrection, I kept looking at Michael from afar. He also turned and looked at me a couple of times. When after the service he came to talk to me, I felt happier than Jesus must have after he discovered that he had been resurrected.

We walked out together. We caught up and spoke about school. He had become a partner at his father's investment bank almost immediately after college. I told him about Columbia, and we decided to get together during the week. And it finally happened! We dated for a whole year.

However, there is no Paradise Island if my mother happens to live there too. My mother has hated his family ever since they tried to take advantage of her foundation's investments, which were managed by their bank. They invested some of the money in failing corporations, in which Michael's family happened to have majority ownership. This sad chapter of my mother's life ended in a considerable asset loss for her pet project. And in New York, most of these wealthy families rate each other primarily through the success or failure of their mutual investments.

When my mother found out I was dating Michael, she decided immediately to stop our relationship. Talk about being anal! She told me that Michael had developed a reputation for being a womanizer and that I should stop dating him. As if we were living in the 17th century, and instructions from here were going to deter me!

She mentioned that gossip to me only once. But I knew there was not an important relationship in my mother's life that she didn't try to control. It turned out that she immediately hired an investigator, unbeknownst to me, to find out if Michael was being disloyal to me.

My mother visited me the night after my first session with *Super* and showed me photos of Michael holding a baby while walking with a woman. The investigator's report stated that he was living with her on the West Side of Manhattan. He had gotten married eight months ago in a private ceremony at City Hall after she, his girlfriend, became pregnant. Her name was Lucy McCarthy. She was the daughter of a partner of Michael's father in the investment bank.

I was extremely shocked because Michael had an apartment in the East Village, where we spent a lot of time together when we weren't in my apartment. No wonder we never went to restaurants in the City. We mostly stayed in his apartment or my apartment, ordering takeout. I didn't know why at that time.

I did know that many women would never let a catch like Michael escape under any circumstances. Maybe his marriage was predicated on that basis. Or maybe it was caused by Michael's sick old habit of wanting women to get pregnant to prove his total macho control over them, while counting on the women rendering him blameless by having an abortion. In any case it was clear that he had gotten his wife pregnant, that she had refused to get an abortion, and that they had married. Michael was more hypocritical than the fabled Trojan horse.

# CHAPTER SEVEN

After my mother left my apartment, I remained in shock, crying off and on all night. First, on my initial day at work I had the worst time I could remember because of an uncooperative client who wanted to kill himself and didn't have any respect for me – making me feel that I was the most racist person on earth. Hours later I learned that the love of my life was not who I thought he was – and not for the better. He was a cheating liar. And on top of that I had to watch the great pleasure it gave my mother to break up our relationship.

I called Michael and I asked him to come over. He was still working in the bank. He insisted on knowing why he should come that night, and I told him that we needed to talk in person, and that it was an emergency. He came to the apartment in a bad mood. Immediately after entering the apartment, he said, "What did you call me for? Today is not a good day."

"It's worse than you think," I said. "I called you because I know."

"What are you talking about? What do you know?"

"I know that you've been lying to me."

"About what? Why don't you tell me the lie?"

"Why don't you tell me?! I just found out that you have a wife and a baby. I think that can be considered a big problem."

"How did you? I... I'm separated from her."

"Her? You called her 'HER' – or is it 'WIFE'?"

Then I saw him smirk.

"Wipe that smirk from your face! Look at me. Do I look like a slut? Do I look like a slut to you?"

"Our marriage is based on business. She is the daughter of my father's partner. Her pregnancy was an accident. I had to marry her."

"Now it makes sense what people told me about you – that you are fake – a fake in all your business dealings – and now you are doing the same with me and her."

His tone changed. "I don't want to leave. This isn't the way to end this relationship. You need to let me get a divorce! Let's not end this way!"

"You ended it, not me!" I yelled back.

…As he was opening the door to leave, he turned and looked at me. I grabbed his keys and threw them at him. "Oh, and by the way, take the keys to your fucking bachelor's pad." They hit him in the shoulder and fell to the ground. He picked them up and left.

Something I have never been able to do in my life is to forgive deception. Our relationship was as dead as a ghost with impotence.

# CHAPTER EIGHT
## *The Second Session*

There is a misunderstanding that therapists have their lives in order and have learned how to not be vulnerable to frustration and stress. I have often heard people say this. In graduate school I thought that we were going to learn how to live a stress-free life. All of us did. We thought that the psychological education that we were acquiring would make us happier and more 'well-adjusted' than the rest of society. Don't ever think that your therapist is a superman or a superwoman. We can be under as much stress as anyone else. I think that's why it is recommended that therapists also attend therapy in order to deal better with clients, and with their own lives.

Well, after the previous day and night, I felt like the most disturbed person in the world. And on top of that I had to try to help a man with a mean disposition toward me and everyone else. Worst of all, people from all of the various cultures in the world would have agreed that I had no idea what I was doing. No one who knew what was happening would believe that I could help him at all, least of all my client himself. I felt like an immature child with a master's degree that I didn't deserve. If that day anyone would have asked me for a therapist I would have said, "Do not go to a therapist. Go to an astrologer. They are cheaper and quicker, at making you feel good in only one session."

And there I was, ready to meet for the second time, the suicidal client from hell. I was in my office drying my tears, straightening my clothes and hair with my shaking hands. I was vainly trying to look like a presentable professional woman. In other words, I looked like shit. Nevertheless, there I was telling myself that I would go through with this.

Then *Super* entered the office. We stared at each other, but I was so depressed that I couldn't even smile. I stuck to the practice of allowing the client to speak first, even though I didn't believe that technique would work. We stared at each other for just a couple of seconds. Suddenly, and to my surprise, he spoke.

"I hope you don't mind if I share an important therapeutic thought that just came to me."

"By all means! Please, go ahead." Then he pointed immediately at the chair and said, "You didn't change the fucking chair. Did you?"

I thought to myself, "Thank you God for being with me always and never abandoning me as you just did." And then I replied to him, "I apologize. Sorry! I told them to get a new one. It will be here soon."

He didn't say anything else and continued staring at me. Then he exploded: "Why do you always have to wait for me to say something when I come here? Am I missing some rules?"

"I already told you… I'm here for you. You go first."

"You don't seem to be in a good mood today. Are you okay *Columbia*?"

That was the last thing I wanted to hear that day, the word 'Columbia.' Once again, he read my psychological state, and he didn't have a degree in clinical therapy. He was ready to humiliate me. My sarcasm has always saved me from driving myself into masochism. I impulsively blurted out something cutting. This time I heard myself saying to him in a snarky way, "I was okay until you called me 'Columbia.'"

I took a deep breath again to let him win the battle of the stares since I wasn't in the mood to play that game again.

He said, "Let me break the ice. What do you do to relax? – I listen to Eddie Palmieri. His music is so violent and sensual that even nuns miles away get wet."

I thought at first that he said that to piss me off, but I could've been wrong. So, I decided to follow his train of thought to see where he would take us. I said, "I'm sure the Pope will be happy to hear why the nuns have been acting weird lately. – Is his music? – What's it called? – Salsa?"

He nodded in the affirmative without saying a word.

I asked, "Why do you like salsa so much?"

"I love salsa because I like slow music more."

"What does that mean?"

"You tell me. You're the therapist here. You can ask me something else if you wish."

His ambiguous answer led me to believe that he seemed to be struggling to escape from sadness. I thought he must be hiding something, but I didn't want to push him too much since he was already talking. Therefore, I decided to respect his wish for me to ask him something else. I asked something that I should have asked in the first session, but never had the chance due to his interruptions and mind games. I asked, "Ok. Tell me about work. How is it? Do you like it?"

"Why are you asking me about my work?"

I gave the normal response, "That's where adults spend most of their day. A lot happens at work that affects us."

"Yeah! I agree. Work is where society reflects itself. Work is a microcosm of society."

I was surprised and responded, "Exactly! Well said!"
I noticed that for some reason his face got more serious after I complimented him. I thought that I had said something wrong. His face kept getting tenser, and then he questioned me, "'Well said?' 'Well said' you said. Why? Did that impress you?"

"Why not? It's true. Work relations usually reflect many of the dynamics of society."

"Let me get this straight. If I say something remotely reasonable, you think 'Wow! I'm impressed with this brown motherfucker. He is not as dumb as I thought.'"

"Let's keep the obscene language out of this conversation as much as we can." I said, trying to keep things under control.

"I bet you also think I am over-sensitive. Don't you?"

"I can't arrive at that conclusion. What's going on? Can you tell me what you are talking about?"

Immediately after I said those words, I felt that – for no reason – retaliation was coming my way, and I was correct.

"You already have me in your 'mind file' completely stereotyped. Your neurons immediately connect my ethnicity, my color, my neighborhood, my accent. Then your neurons become condescending. And if we catch you in your bullshit, then we are too sensitive."

I asked back, "Are your neurons doing the same with me?"

*Super* stood up, upset, and began walking around the office rubbing his back. Then he said, "*Columbia,* listen to this simple secret about people of color. When you are condescending to us, we don't like it."

I realize now that I spoke to him like men of my class usually talk to me, and I don't like it either. But then I didn't know better. Not only that, but my professors at Columbia didn't know better either. These scenarios were not discussed, or if they were, they were brushed off immediately. Moreover, I was subconsciously ready to be more condescending in my next sentence, which was, "OK. I get your point and appreciate that you are sharing this with me. I will take it into consideration."

"You see, right there. That tone, that fucking tone! You are a liberal, aren't you?"

"I fail to see the –" He cut me off.

"A right-winger wouldn't have said a thing, because they don't care about how they are perceived. You liberals say stupid things because you think you are not racist, and you end up saying racist things."

"Well," I said, "it seems that racism has affected you a lot."

"GODDAMNIT, *COLUMBIA*, LISTEN TO YOU! Racism? Like racism has nothing to do with you. Shit, you keep making my point."

I was totally exasperated, so I yelled, "HOW?"

"YOU STILL DON'T GET IT!"

At that moment Joe opened the door and entered the room. He asked, "Is everything OK here?"

I said, "Yes. Don't worry. Everything is fine."

*Super* responded to Joe, "We are cool." Then he turned to me and said, "Was he listening outside the fucking door?"

Joe asked me, "Are you sure you are ok?"

I was so tired that before I could answer *Super* said, "Hey man! You're taking my time."

I then responded, "He's right. Everything is OK. Please let us finish."

Joe was angry to say the least. I felt that this was going to be my last day working there. I had managed due to my naiveté to lose my boyfriend and my first job. But I didn't care anymore, about anything except *Super*. I really didn't want him to leave.

Joe looked at *Super* and said, "OK. I don't want to hear yelling again."

Then he looked at me and said, "Any problems let me know." Joe left.

I'd had it! I was so tired that I went straight at *Super* and said, "I think you are filibustering these sessions with race and politics to avoid talking about yourself.

"I told you already, *Columbia*. You need to hear my reality, not the fiction that makes you comfortable."

I kept at him. "Please understand this; I'm not your enemy! I'm here to work with you. But more importantly, I think it will help our communication if you stop assuming things about me. Perhaps I come from a very poor background. I may even be of mixed race and look white. And the fact that I went to Columbia doesn't necessarily make me a privileged white person."

None of that was true, but that was all that I could do to deflect his attacks.

"Listen *Columbia*, I have worked with working class white people, and they don't sound like you; they don't dress like you; they don't sneeze like you. Even those whites don't like you. You can't help me, you are here to help yourself. Oh! And by the way, nice try! You are white!"

He saw right through me. So I said, "Ah Jesus! You don't want to make things easy for me. Do you? Do you? And yes. I am white."

"I knew it!"

Then I exploded, "OH! You can think whatever the hell you want of me. However, there are not many clinical social workers here. I'm all you have. You understand me? Since you already warned me that we have only four sessions left, why don't you give me a freaking chance? That's all I ask. Damn it, a freaking chance!" It felt good. I don't regret it, since after that moment, he clearly told me why he didn't trust me.

"A chance? I'm here with a girl who graduated from an Ivy League school who thinks the world is what she read about. Which makes me wonder, what chapter in your books was I? And by the way, don't be so prudish. Instead of saying 'freaking,' say 'fucking,' like everybody else. The streets of this City were not made out of cement, but out of vulgarity. So, step out and walk them. This is not Martha's Vineyard. This is fucking New York City!"

"Well, thank you for sharing your experience and advice regarding the pedestrian life of the City. ...So, let me try this again. ...What about your work?"

"Work is easy. I have worked for 40 years as a super in buildings on both the East and the West Side, always in high-end luxury buildings with very demanding, high maintenance tenants."

"Do the tenants treat you poorly?"

"Poorly? If poorly means treating me like shit, then yes. ... Very, very poorly."

"Where are you working now?"

"The building is on the West Side."

"And how is it in that West Side building?"

"If I ever commit suicide, I'm going to blame it on the West Side".

I wanted to keep things going, so I asked, "Is there any difference between the West- and Eastsiders?"

"The Eastsiders say, 'Oh! You want a holiday bonus? Fuck you!' The Westsiders at least give you a $20.00 tip, as if they were feeding an animal in the zoo. Westsiders think about what they do for you, not what you do for them."

"And the Eastsiders?"

"Eastsiders are more pissed off than Jim Crow Mississippians the day they found out about the Brown vs. the Board of Education decision. Very pissed off Mississippians."

"What? Never mind. What about the Westsiders?"

"Westsiders can't be accused of being very pissed off Jim Crow Mississippians like the Eastsiders. That would be politically catastrophic for them."

I tried to clarify, "So.... The Eastsiders are less hypocritical than the Westsiders? Is that what you mean?"

"Good, *Columbia*. You're getting good."

"Well, and you are getting condescending."

"Perhaps you are the one who is too sensitive!" He smiled and continued, "Let me make it simple for you. The Eastsiders and the Westsiders are like the Republican and Democratic Parties. One hates us. The other pretends to like us!"

"I have to admit that I'm learning a lot," I said and was sincere about it.

"You really need me to keep coming here."

"Sorry," I said, "time's up."

"*Columbia*, every morning I open my eyes disappointed that I'm still alive. You have three sessions left."

At the end of the session, I accepted my mistakes and felt more comfortable with him calling me '*Columbia*.' This time, I didn't complain about it as much as I complained during our first session. But I was still torn. Obviously, calling me '*Columbia*' was his way of expressing his disdain for people like me. Maybe that was the most honest information I was getting from him. However, I asked myself if the level of therapeutic license that I was allowing him was good for his therapy. Well, I didn't know, and perhaps it was too late for me to question that anyway. But there was no doubt that I was going to find out sooner rather than later. The tone of our relationship had been established, and he obviously controlled it. At that moment I didn't see that as something negative. This therapy was about his reality, not mine. Only time would tell if my therapeutic intervention was working or not.

## CHAPTER NINE

### *Supervision with Joe*

The supervision session with Joe was scheduled right after my session with *Super*. Before my meeting, I had asked Joe by email to get new chairs for the office – not only for me, but for *Super,* who got back pains that impeded him from sitting comfortably in the existing chair. When none arrived, I sent Joe a second email, and still he hadn't brought the new chairs to the office.

I didn't think that supervision was going to be different from what I had at Columbia. But this experience definitely opened my eyes to how supervision works in the real world. Everybody is rushing to finish one thing, to start another that needs to be finished as soon as possible, so that they can start another one. That means that there is no bullshit allowed in the dialogue. The supervisor goes straight to the point with no finesse or fancy professional protocols. I had so many issues to discuss, but many were personal, and Joe wasn't the right person with whom to talk about them anyway.

I was surprised that I was able to concentrate on my case somewhat after breaking up with Michael. If anything, *Super* had helped me to keep my mind off Michael enough to be a functional human being – albeit one with a broken heart. I hate to do it, but I have to give credit to my mother for this. I needed something to keep my mind off Michael, and this case did it perfectly.

Something those two sessions with *Super* had taught me was that I was in the minority when compared with the rest of humanity. Stupid me! I really thought that society was more or less like me. My unconscious perceptions of class removed me from the world that surrounded me.

What I knew about poverty was from things I heard vicariously and read. Therefore, I saw society's poor mostly on film or through TV shows and viewed them as part of entertaining dramas or comedies. When I accidentally drove through poor neighborhoods of color, instead of looking around, my instinct was to hurry to avoid viewing a new reality. On some subconscious level I pretended that what I saw was temporary, like a documentary film. Further, when I went with my parents to our home upstate, we never – not even once – passed through Harlem. Despite the fact that I lived only a mile away, I didn't know what Harlem looked like until I took the train to work there.

There I was, waiting for Joe to come to my office. I was pacing desperately around the office until he finally opened the door. And then, once he came in, I exploded without planning to or recognizing that I was out of control. I yelled at him, "First, you can't interrupt us like that anymore. Second, you need to get him a better chair. Third, you need to TRUST ME!"

He responded, "First, that chair is a very expensive chair. It cost us ten dollars at the Salvation Army. Second, I should have thrown him out of here right after he yelled at me. Third, my concern is for your safety. Therefore, he has to go!"

After that answer I learned something about Joe; he was not a pushover. I wanted to show him that neither was I. My inexperience and pride allowed me to take crap from my client, but not from a supervisor that depended on my mother to keep his business afloat. So, I fought back for my client.

"NO WAY! You can't ask him to leave. He's very educated, but he hates the stereotype that we have of him."

"That we have of him? How did 'we' become part of the 'we' problem?"

"I meant society. I think I'm benefiting more from my client than he is from me. My arrogance has."

"Don't go there! Don't go there!" Joe said.

"I feel like an upper-class white tyrant." I replied.

"Don't go there! Don't go there! You are going to drive yourself crazy. I've seen it before. I understand we have done some fucked up things in this society! However, you will be okay as long as you ignore the history of this country! – It's like watching a bad TV show. You change the channel, and it goes away."

"Why?" I said. "Don't we have to reflect on our interactions with our clients?"

Joe shook his head. "That's not a reflection. That's white liberal masochism. You are a millionaire. Nobody is perfect!"

"You are just another white person telling me that. You have a vested interest in protecting your ego, like me."

"What interest?" Joe asked.

"Power. Privilege. Control."

"Since when have you become the female Malcolm X?"

When he said that, I said to myself, "Where did I hear that name before?"

Then he continued with his political advice, "Let the whites at the ACLU feel guilty. You need to focus. Focus! Right now, you are more out of focus than a film student at NYU!"

"Don't you think that the best therapy is to have equality in society?" I asked.

"I bet *Super* said that too. Listen, your job is to help him where he's at psychologically, not politically! Your revolution is to help him to save his own fucking life, not to march with him in the streets."

"What do you want me to do?" I shrugged. "That's all he talks about, all the time!"

"What the hell were you expecting? He is an activist. That's what activists talk about all the time. Activists only talk about politics and race."

I had already spent two sessions with *Super*. I had read his file. I thought that I already had an idea what my client was like, at least politically, so sarcasm flew out of my mouth like a missile, "No! Really? Is that what it is? Politics and race? Oh my God! ...And I thought he was talking about the decaying flora in Central Park during autumn."

"Don't be a smart ass! The reason I'm reminding you is because you forgot something."

"What did I forget?" I said, sounding even more sarcastic.

"That even activists have families. Find out about his family. Don't try to be the white Messiah. The fact that you think that you can talk politics with him makes his point."

"And his point is...?" I said raising my eyebrows.

I disagreed with him, but I shouldn't have asked that question in that tone. He went nuts, "His point is that you are the arrogant, condescending, white liberal bitch who thinks she knows better than him how to fight the exploitation and racism that YOU REPRESENT! GODDAMMIT, HE IS MESSING WITH YOU. HE IS PLAYING YOU. OPEN YOUR EYES! THERE IS URGENCY HERE. HE IS HIDING SOMETHING! GODDAMMIT! It's time to ask him about his family. His family! You hear me? His family. Not this political bull."

"I KNOW HE IS HIDING SOMETHING!" I yelled back. "But it is not the only thing affecting him. It is everything. Every experience counts. I have to deal with his social, economic, and political context."

Never use sarcasm with a cynic, especially if he has thirty years of experience beyond yours in the field of therapy.

He said, "Oh! I get it! Stupid inexperienced me! When am I going to learn? How could I have missed the fucking point? Of course! 'It's the social, economic and political context.' LISTEN, Ms. White Rosa Parks, you are already sitting in the front of the bus; stretch your legs, relax, and enjoy THE RIDE! The ride around your head that he is giving you. He is dancing circles around you."

Then he suddenly stopped and took a deep breath. I think that he realized who my mother was and said, "Ok. Let's do it your way."

"Thank you," I said.

"Please, make sure you send my regards to your mother. Tell her I can't wait to talk to her again," he said.

I said, "Fucking asshole," under my breath.

"I heard that! I heard that! FUCKING MILLENNIALS!" He left slamming the door the same way Michael did when I asked him to leave the apartment. I've always wondered, what is it with men slamming doors after a woman implies or says they are assholes.

# CHAPTER TEN
## *The Third Session*

I was still shaken by my supervision session with Joe as I was about to start my third session with *Super*. Michael's betrayal was still in my mind as well. I was furious, but in a strange way. I thought I was managing things well, and that all this upset was not affecting my concentration on the case. Perhaps, I thought, crises unconsciously force us to focus a bit more on another thing in order to protect our sanity.

An interesting note: Michael had called me the night before and wanted to meet in two days, on Friday, after my fourth session with *Super*. I hoped that session would go well so that I would be able to deal effectively with Michael. The truth is that I don't know why I agreed to meet him. There was nothing that could bring us together. As I said before, this relationship was deader than a ghost with impotence. Today, I desperately needed a breakthrough from *Super*. It was vital that we make progress. I decided that I needed to trust my instincts.

By now I could really appreciate Joe's wisdom in deciding to give me only one case to start my career. It would have been impossible to start with a whole caseload while I was going through what I was going through.

Then *Super* entered. Showtime! I saw him and I felt ready. No more waiting to see who talks first. I fired immediately, "Let me ask you something out of the blue."

"Like you always do?" he responded.

I felt really relaxed for some reason, so I accepted his mocking me and said immediately, "Please. Ah, I'm trying here!"

"Go ahead."

I might have been projecting, but I asked, "Do you sleep well at night?"

*Super* gave me a long look with a long pause. Then he said, "Every morning I wake up with my hands buried in my pillow trying to find one good dream, but instead I find them covered with the mud of my nightmares."

"Describe them."

"I forget them."

"Writing helps to remember important things." I offered. "Have you ever sat down to write a diary about your life?"

"My heart is my pen. My skin is my paper, and my spirit is my writer. Can you read my pain?"

"That's the problem." I said. "I can't read you at all!"

"Then you're an illiterate therapist!" he shot back.

"Thank you so much for the compliment. Now, back to you, if you don't mind. Who influenced you the most when you were young?"

"My mother."

"What do you remember the most about her?"

He thought for a while then he said, "There is a thought that I can't ever shake out of my mind. I remember her taking me to the supermarket every Friday after she got paid shit for 48 hours of work sitting in front of a sewing machine. I thought the supermarket was a church because she prayed there so much. She prayed with her eyes like laser beams straight on the cash register as the amount got higher and higher, item after item. I still see myself looking up at her, holding the bottom of her dress as she leaned against the cash register with one hand trembling, squeezing my hand, with the other hand holding her grocery bag like a precious baby. Two babies in two hands. I saw her returning food to the cashier in shame. I also saw neighborhood people saying to her, 'Do not worry Margarita. I'll help to pay for it.' And my mother accepted their money, swallowing her pride like the Chrysler building sinking down her throat. I watched my mother go through that every Friday. Fifty years after her passing I still see her in front of that cash register as clearly as I see you now."

He kept going, "She didn't go to buy groceries. She went to purgatory! So, *Columbia*, when you are in line trying to get the cashier's attention because the line is too slow, please be patient. Don't rush the fucking line. Don't yell at the people in front of you to hurry up. Just ahead of you, maybe, just maybe, there is a woman counting pennies and quarters, praying. And no one, no one should yell at her; ever."

He was fighting to hold back his tears. I was praying for him to let go, but he kept crunching every muscle in his face. Clenching his fists like he clenched his mother's dress when he was a child. This time he didn't have anyone who would hold his trembling hands to make him feel secure. His head was down as if he was embarrassed and trying not to look at me. I wanted to say something meaningful. I wanted to cry with him even though he was hiding his tears. I wanted to show my empathy, but I didn't know how to do that in a professional way. I was actually proud that I didn't break down.

The best way to help your client is by being as objective as possible. That doesn't mean that you don't have feelings, or you don't care. The clients come to see you for your objectivity and compassion. The sessions can't be dominated by your emotions about your clients. One of the key objectives should be to help your clients as they are at that moment, and not as you would like them to be. Most clients take time to get there. The limitation of only five sessions set by the insurance company for *Super* certainly was an obstacle in reaching the ultimate goal for his therapy. But my training required that I should be collected and let this moment live for him. So, I paused for a while, and then I said, "Thank you for sharing that." I knew I needed to help him to continue talking about the same subject. So, I urged him to go further, "You said during intake that she died. How did she die?"

"She got arrested while striking the company. She died from a heart attack in the precinct building. Now you know why I am the way I am. That's the influence you asked me about."

"How old were you?"

"Ten."

"Did your father raise you?"

"Never met him. He died in Vietnam when I was really little. I lived in homes until 13, when I became a super's assistant, and later – a super. Even when I went to college, I was a super. Enough!" he said.

"I think that you have been feeling lonely and sad from when your mother died until this day. I wonder if your mother's death has anything to do with your suicidal thoughts?"

"When I was told that my mother died…"

I opened my big mouth and interrupted him, "Did you attempt…"

Then it was his turn to interrupt me, "Can I finish my fucking thought, *Columbia*?"

"I'm sorry. Please continue."

He started again, "I thought that my mother and I were going to be together forever…"

"What about your wife?  Is she still around?"

"She left."

"Why?"

"Dishonesty," he said. "Honesty should be everything in life, but not in a marriage."

"Why not?" I asked.

"You are so young *Columbia*. You have to be able to look one another in the eye and say, 'I still love you.' …Even when you are not sure anymore. Lying is the basis for a good marriage."

His last answer came close to home. Lying was not unique to him. I do relate to lying. How could he lie to his wife? Suddenly I wanted to confront him, and I said, "But that's a contradiction!"

"It is not a contradiction," he countered. "It's marriage. Marriage is the only war where you have to kiss the enemy in the morning. *Columbia*, lying can be an expression of love."

I felt angry at his casual response, but I realized I needed to gather myself, so that I wouldn't make the most unprofessional comment in the annals of clinical psychology. So, I collected myself and responded, "Please tell me how lying can express love?"

"*Columbia*, love doesn't have to be authentic; it has to be believable!"

The compassion I felt for him just minutes ago disappeared immediately, like snow falling on fire. That's how Michael treated me. I was seeing myself as *Super's* wife, and *Super* as another version of Michael. So, I asked him about his wife as if I were asking Michael if he ever loved me.

"Do you love your wife?"

"I do, very much."

"What?" I thought to myself. "Can you love someone and lie to her?" I had to tell him that I wasn't following him at all! "I have to admit. I'm lost here. I don't understand. Why are you saying that there is nothing wrong with a lie and that you still love her?"

*Super* bounced out of the chair and grabbed it and threw it to the floor. "THIS FUCKING CHAIR!"

I immediately stood up – very nervous and afraid – but I managed to control myself. I said to myself that either he kills me here, or this is a breakthrough for him. I took the risk of believing that it was a breakthrough. What I didn't know was whether his breakthrough was affecting me in relation to my relationship to Michael. It's very difficult to counsel your client when you can't even counsel yourself, especially when the issue being confronted by both the client and therapist seems so similar. I was afraid that I was going to find answers related to why Michael lied to me. And now I was hearing that another man had done the same thing that Michael did to me, and I simply could not fathom the idea that I was trying to help him, "I'm asking you again why you say that love can be a lie. How can it be a lie?"

He yelled at me, "Because SHE WAS THE ONE WHO LIED TO ME! I NEVER LIED TO HER. I never stopped loving her!" Then he pointed to the door and said, "IS THE MOTHERFUCKER HERE?"

I felt relieved and stupid at the same time. Rule number one is: NEVER bring your feelings into therapy if you really want to be a good therapist. And that's exactly what I did. I was confused about the whole session, and myself. Rule number two: You don't have to like your client in order to help, as long as you do your best to help. If you can't do that, it's time to tell the client that you cannot work with him or her. However, I did feel relieved that, despite his treatment of me, I always liked *Super*. I just didn't want him to be an adulterous liar. The fact that his wife was the one that lied to him was enough for me. I told him, "No. Joe is not here today. But please, be more specific about her lying!"

"I already told you. You're too young; you need to be betrayed – deceived – to understand it. Pray it never happens to you."

Once again, I was shaken by the coincidence. Pray that doesn't happen to me? He didn't notice how shaken I was when he said those words. I kept asking questions, not only to help him find more clarity about his situation. I was trying to find answers about Michael's betrayal through *Super's* words. I felt so unprepared and unprofessional in using my client to decipher my boyfriend's conduct toward me. But I couldn't shake off the similarities, and they caught me completely unprepared. So, in my fear that there was a possibility that Michael never loved me, I selfishly asked

*Super*, "Do you think that she may still love you, even though she lied and betrayed you?"

"Love is too depressing," he said. "Can we talk about my suicide?"

"Why did she leave?" I asked.

"I never met my wife's standards. When I looked at her, I wanted to be more, but I failed. She had been seeing another man for years. My wife waited until our daughter graduated from high school, and then she moved in with him."

"How did you feel the moment she left?"

"I wanted to die so badly that I could have shot myself in the head with the gunfire of my thoughts!"

"Did she marry him?"

"No, not yet I guess."

"After all this time, do you still consider her a hypocrite?"

"Well, she now lives on the West Side!"

"Come on!" I said. "Does your daughter know what happened?"

"She knows. She finished law school, got married, and has a daughter. She lives in California."

"How is your relationship with your daughter?"

"Great," he said. "But she's not here anymore. I'm alone."

"But now you are not totally alone. You are here with me now."

"*Columbia*. Let's get real. You're here because you get paid $150.00 for 45 minutes of work. You, therapists, are the whores of the subconscious!"

"Oh my God! That's the best compliment you have given me so far. Thank you, *Super*!" I said with fake enthusiasm.

"Ah! Don't mention it. I'm here to help!" he replied in a professional tone.

"If you don't mind," I said, moving forward, "I would like to change the topic from my career of psychological prostitution to you! Since you have been coming here, how strong is your desire to end your life now?"

"My suicide is waiting around the corner, ready to mug me," he said. And continued, "Do you know what I think about you and me?"

I have to admit that I was a bit sarcastic when I responded, "I can't wait for you to tell me!"

"You know the play 'Waiting for Godot?"

"Yes, what about it?"

"We are like Vladimir and Estragon, talking bullshit while waiting for something to come to give us some meaning, – but it never comes. My biggest fear in life was always to be insignificant. I live the reality of that fear every second of my existence. I have amputated my soul while trying to amputate my pain. I am already dead."

Then he walked straight towards the window. I panicked, "Where are you going? Please don't go to the window. I understand very well the pain you talk about."

He stopped and turned towards me, "You understand? How?"

"I do. Believe me. I do. Please come back here."

"Why should I trust you?" he asked.

"Because I'm bound by confidentiality. Because I don't have emotions at stake here, which helps me to be objective. Thus, I can help you to find a solution without letting my emotions interfere. Only your feelings count. You need to trust me!"

"Why should I trust you if you have nothing at stake?"

I said, "I don't have a reason to betray you either."

"I told you already, you are too young. You don't know what betrayal is yet."

"Yes," I said, "I do! I do! People who love you can fail you and betray you sometimes." I couldn't control myself after I said those words. This time I turned my back and began weeping.

*Super* kept going, "You are so naïve *Columbia*. Real love can never betray you. There is no betrayal when there is love."

Then he noticed my reaction and said, "Why are you sobbing?"
I automatically gave the normal apologetic reply while sniffling, "I'm so sorry."

His voice softened and he seemed to move from being dismissive to being genuinely concerned when he said, "Are you okay sweetheart?"

He called me 'sweetheart'! I felt those words like feathers landing on my shoulders. He is what I thought he was, a bundle of heart. All the sad and tough moments in the last few weeks were only masquerading his humanity. "Sorry," I said, wanting to move forward, "I have allergies. Please, continue."

He asked again, "Are you sure you're okay?"

"Yes… What about your daughter? Have you thought what would happen to her if you kill yourself?"

"If I kill myself, she will go into therapy with someone like you, who will confuse her even more. What's wrong?"

"Sorry," I said, "I don't feel well. Time is up anyway."

"I've been too rough on you? I always destroy everything. It's me, is it? I'm sorry!"

"No," I replied, "it has nothing to do with you. I'm just a bit sick."

*Super* began walking toward the door saying, "I curse everything around me. Maybe I shouldn't be here."

"You made a deal with me. Just two more sessions." I reminded him.

"*Columbia*, listen. When you get older you will understand what I am about to tell you. It's in the solitude of your dreams that you find the real mirror of yourself. I don't need therapy. This is over."

"Just one more question. Please!"

"What?"

"What are you going to do now"?

"I don't know. The future is always silent."

"YOU HAVE TO RETURN. KEEP YOUR WORD. YOU HAVE TO KEEP YOUR WORD!"

And he left, like a breeze blowing the feathers off my shoulders. But I thought it was a bluff. He wanted to live. I know he wanted to live. I ran to supervision. I needed to talk to Joe.

# CHAPTER ELEVEN
## *Second Supervision with Joe*

I opened Joe's door and entered. Joe was typing something, and I caught him by surprise. He said, "Hey! What the hell are you doing here? Our meeting is in half an hour."

I ignored what he said and started talking at the speed of light, "His marriage failed after 30 years. She had an affair with another man. He didn't know. I don't think I can function as his therapist anymore. I'm not being helpful."

"What the hell are you talking about?"

"*Super*! Remember? The case you gave me. His wife left him for another man."

"Stop talking so fast and stop walking around like a chicken with its head cut off. Calm down. And this affected you how?"

"It touched me suddenly in a way I didn't anticipate. It's triggering deep feelings about my personal life."

"You made it personal when you let him call you *Columbia*."

"Yes, I messed up! I messed up! The good thing is that I don't think he thinks of me anymore like a typical 'Westsider'."

"Calm down! What does that mean? 'Westsider'?"

"Like a white, upper class, liberal hypocrite from the West Side."

"Damn! I just moved there."

"I cried in front of him when he told me about his wife's betrayal."

"What? What did you say? You cried? You fucking cried!?!? Therapists don't cry in therapy! The clients do! Your job is to hand them

77

the tissues, not to use them yourself. What the hell is going on here? Tell Me! TELL ME!"

I had to come clean. There was no other way. All I had was Joe! "I'm pregnant!"

Michael did it to me as he did it to so many in prep school. I bet he put on the condom and then took it off without letting me know, as he did with those girls. The pill made my hormones go wild, so I trusted my boyfriend and the condom company. And having sex did indeed feel different on one occasion. Sadly, when you are in the mood, you're apt to dispense certain liberties to your lover that later become your chains.

I continued, "But it gets worse…"

"Pregnant? Worse?"

"I think I love him! I love him."

"SUPER? YOU FUCKED SUPER?"

"NOOO! I'm talking about my boyfriend. He is married."

"Earth, please, swallow me and shit me through Antarctica! Well, let me tell you. It really got worse! You are an adulterer!"

"Legally," I said, "he is the adulterer. Out there, I'm the whore!"

"I couldn't agree more." said Joe.

"Thank you so much for your empathy Joe!"

"May I ask – what about the pregnancy?" he responded.

"Maybe I will keep it." I said.

"Can I ask why?"

"I'm Catholic."

"Then, switch religions. Worship your smartphone… like everybody else!"

"How will I answer to God?" I asked.

"Don't worry. God doesn't need to ask questions. He knows about everything, including fucked up people."

"I don't know what to do." I said, and continued, "God can be so exhausting!"

"It's not God who is exhausting you. Your head is. You have transformed yourself into a 70's urban revolutionary billionaire, like fucking Patty Hearst. You just got pregnant by your boyfriend who happens to be married. You live in the hypocritical West Side of Manhattan. You have been talking lately like fucking Karl Marx, not to mention that now you think you are Puerto Rican! Which is, by the way, the most dramatic transference of personality ever recorded in the annals of clinical therapy!"

I replied, "I really think he will commit suicide."

"Listen carefully!" Joe said. "And never forget this. Never! Every suicidal person confuses suicide with a painkiller. My concern now is you. You are fucked up!"

"I know. I know. I'm so confused… Perhaps he will divorce his wife and marry me."

"There is only one situation more pathetic than having a married boyfriend."

"Oh, please illuminate me! And that is…?" I said sarcastically.

"It is a young woman who thinks that her married boyfriend will divorce his wife and leave his children to marry her!"

"I didn't know he was married!" I yelled back in frustration. "I was in love, and he fooled me." I shifted the focus back to *Super*. "I know that *Super* will be back. I know it. If I fail to break through in the next session, I will resign. He called me 'sweetheart' when I cried. Perhaps, unconsciously, he sees me now like a daughter. I need to ask him about his real daughter."

Joe had a weakness that he couldn't control. He was often simultaneously sarcastic and cynical at the wrong moment. He proved this by saying, "Finally! Now you are thinking. You got it! Now I know you can do it, *Columbia*!"

I yelled back, "Fuck you!"

Joe showed me his middle finger and said, "I went to CUNY. So, fuck you!" And he left his own office.

## CHAPTER TWELVE
### *The Fourth Session*

I called *Super,* but he didn't answer. I left messages asking him to come in for at least one more session. Again, he didn't respond. Somehow though I had a strong feeling that he would return. I knew for some inexplicable reason that he felt bad for leaving. I think he left knowing that I care. And there I was, in the office waiting. Our appointment time was at 5:00 PM. It was already 5:30 PM, and he had not arrived. I gave up and opened the door to leave. There he was, standing at the door as if he had been there all the time. I was happily surprised. So, I said, "Oh, you came. How long have you been here?"

"Since 5 PM. I was thinking about what to say to apologize."

"It's good to see you." I said. "Come in. I wonder what made you come back."

*Super* looked at me and pointed at the chair, "I came back because I missed the fucking chair!"

"Sorry about that. I told the director about it."

"I understand. It's OK. Go ahead. You start," he said.

"I want to talk about your mother again. When she died, did you feel as if she abandoned you?"

"I thought she left me. I was angry. Still, I went to bed thinking that she was coming back to wake me up. That's when I began thinking about not being in this world anymore. When I was ten, I just wanted to follow my mother."

"Long time feeling that way wasn't it?" I said. "Do you see any resemblance between your wife and your mother?"

"Oh! Please. This isn't about an Oedipus Complex! Now you want to complicate things."

"It is complicated, but you have to deal with it. Did you feel like your mother betrayed you?"

"My mother didn't betray me. She died. My wife betrayed me!"

I kept going… "Your mother died, and you wanted to die. Your wife deserted you, and you want to die. When people who are not as smart as you order you around, you want to escape. Every departure, every rejection, is an abandonment to you. I don't think you have pleasant thoughts. Who makes you smile when you dream?"

"My daughter."

"OK," I said. "Tell me more about your daughter."

"She thought I was the funniest person in the world. I made her laugh all the time, you know. She went to a very expensive private school. I once went to the school in my *Super* jumpsuit and everybody stared at me. I didn't want to embarrass my daughter, so I never went back."

"How did you afford to pay for such an expensive school?"

"My wife was a teacher. UFT. Good union salary and benefits. I also made more money by living in East Harlem and renting out the apartment that went with my job. That way we could save more money for her schooling. And you know about my part-time job catering. That job almost destroyed my relationship with my daughter."

"How?"

"For her senior prom she needed an expensive dress. So, I accepted an advance for a night gig. During the school's senior prom, they had a ritual where the parents danced a waltz with their children. All that crap only your rich people do."

"Stop it." I said. "Leave me out of it. Go ahead."

"It was her last night in the school, so I felt like it was OK to just go. However, the night before, the catering service called me saying that I had to cater on the night of the prom. Guess where?"

"No! Please tell me it's not true!"

"Yes, her senior prom."

"Oh, my God! No! No! No!" I was shaking my head in disbelief.

"My wife told me not to work, but I had already spent the money. I had to work the prom. I had to."

"What did you do?"

"I told her and my wife to ignore me. I went there knowing that I would be ordered around by her friends and their parents. My daughter saw all that. I saw my wife and daughter talking to the other parents, and I wasn't, you know... My daughter looked so beautiful."

*Super* began sobbing and took a moment to gather his wits. But I was not going to let him find an excuse not to continue, especially when he was breaking through. Yes. I was being unorthodox, but from now on – no more books or theories. It was going to be two human beings just talking. So I said, "You can't stop now. Keep going. Keep going."

*Super* answered, "I was paralyzed... gasping for air. The walls were closing on me. All the parents and kids were yelling at me, telling me to get more drinks. I couldn't move. Suddenly in the middle of that multitude of millionaires ordering me around, I turned and found myself face-to-face with my daughter. She looked straight at me. She was crying, crying but didn't say anything. I couldn't say anything either. Then time suddenly stopped, and in slow motion, she turned and walked away crying. I embarrassed her."

"You can't stop now. Please go on! Go on!" I said.

"Then, the waltz began. I saw the kids running toward their parents and beginning to dance. I saw neither my wife nor my daughter. I had ruined my daughter's dream night. I had fucked it up again… like I thought I had fucked it up with you in the last session. The daughters were dancing the waltz with their fathers, and my daughter wasn't… because I was there as a waiter and had to work. So, I went to get more drinks when I felt a hand on my shoulder. I looked behind me and my daughter was staring at me, tears pouring from those big, beautiful eyes. I thought that she was going to let me have it for messing up her night. She said… She said…"

"What did she say?" I said, on the edge of my seat.

"She said, 'I want to dance with my father.' I said, 'Do not embarrass yourself. Please go and dance with your mother. Don't worry, people will understand'."

"What did she say?"

"She said, 'I have dreamt all year of dancing this waltz with you.' I told her to go away and not embarrass herself. She said, 'Please, don't embarrass me.' Then she held my arms and raised them high and made me dance! We danced and the walls moved away from me. She hugged me like an open book that suddenly closes, kissing a word as if it were its own heart. When the music stopped…, her friends asked her why she was dancing with the waiter. She told them all, 'He is my Papi,' and we both walked away. My daughter is the only person who has never rejected me. I'm afraid that one day she will."

"I know why you came back today, and I think you know it too. It's your love for your daughter. You may not want to admit it, but no one – no one – is fighting to live more than you. Now, I want you to talk about the third time you attempted to end your life. What happened?"

"The night before the prom I stepped on the ledge outside my kitchen window. I didn't look down hoping that a misstep would do it. I thought about what I was about to do to her if I killed myself before her prom. Besides my daughter, nothing could have stopped me that night. The morning after the prom my wife got up early. She was singing in the kitchen. It made me smile. Then she came to bed, lay down next to me, and hugged me tight like never before. She told me how proud she was of our daughter, and me. Then she left for work and never came back again. My wife woke up singing that morning. I thought it was because of me. She must love that man a lot – a lot! …Time is up. Am I right?"

"Your daughter needs you," I said.

"That was a long time ago. She has a lot to live for and be happy about – a daughter, a husband, and a career. She doesn't need me."

"How can you possibly know that she doesn't need you?"

"If she needs me, she is in trouble."

"You are doing much better," I said. "I can see it. And I know that you know it too"

"It's time. Bye," he said, standing up.

"We have one more session," I reminded him.

"I'll be back!" he said, like he meant it.

I said, "Thank you, God."

# CHAPTER THIRTEEN
## *Michael, The Ex-Boyfriend*

I was walking to the bar to meet Michael. He had called repeatedly during the last two days asking me to meet him. His latest phone call persuaded me to go when he said that he just wanted to see me one more time. I struggled with deciding how to proceed. I wasn't so sure if I should tell him that I was pregnant since I wasn't sure yet what I was going to do.

I thought that if I had the baby it would ruin his marriage. I am not that type of woman, regardless of how much I loved him. Men like Michael, I thought, would never stop sleeping around until they were so old that their good looks disappeared. My tentative plan was to disappear from New York and go back to Boston after my last session with *Super*, perhaps to start a new life as a therapist with or without a baby. The progress that I was making with *Super,* based on our last session, gave me the confidence to start a new life without any help from my family.

So, I entered a restaurant/bar in the basement of an old building on the corner of 96th Street and Amsterdam Avenue. It was full of professionals in their mid-twenties and thirties who congregated there after work. I noticed for the first time that I was making comparisons among neighborhoods and cultures with some direct knowledge. In this case the comparison was between the West Side and East Harlem.

Perhaps the last week and a half of working in *El Barrio* helped me to mature more and understand society better. In the bar everybody was white like me, well dressed, and the music was the same as always – rock and roll. There was only one black couple, and I doubt if there were any Latinos. I wanted to yell at everybody: "WAKE THE FUCK UP!" But of course, I didn't.

Then I noticed Michael sitting at the bar. He was already a bit tipsy, nursing a Brandy Alexander, his favorite drink. He saw me and smiled immediately, as if nothing had happened.

I don't know if it's women's fault that men are confident that they can get away with everything in a relationship. What gives them that extra stupid confidence that everything is going to work in their favor? I really hope that we women are not the cause of the validation that allows them to produce such an idiotic smile. If it's us, then we deserve their stupidity. But not me! I didn't smile back. I just stared at him.

Nonetheless he smiled again and said, "Hi. Thank you for coming. Here, I got your drink. Did you miss me?"

"I am not drinking. And No. I hate you."

He kept smiling. "When you hate, that's when you miss a person the most!"

I shook my head. "Whatever. How is the banking business?"

"Better than ever! Wall Street! It's the gift that keeps giving. Look, I just want to come clean and tell you how I really feel."

"Go ahead. Amuse me." I said, hoping that I sounded like a real bitch, but it is so difficult for me to be bitchy. "Damn it," I thought to myself. "Get it together!" But he ignored my comment as if he didn't believe that I was mad at him. So, the bitchy thing wasn't going to work after all.

Then he said, "Look. I want to come clean. I knew you needed a cleaner, Disney version of a boyfriend. I am not that. So, I lied to you. I played along because I really loved you. Therefore, know this about me. I love you, but I hate fucking social workers. I don't give a shit about immigrants, homeless people, working people, gay people, union people, inequality, 'Black Lives Matter,' and all that bullshit. I'm not a stupid liberal. I have responsibilities as the chair of the building's board. I am not the asshole you think I am. It's my job to make these decisions. Hey, I just noticed – you gained a little bit of weight!"

I was stunned. After all of the awful things he said, he had to say I 'gained weight'? I replied, "What's wrong with you?" the disbelief sounding in my voice, directly followed by sarcasm as I continued, "I'm so glad I came here. Now I know what to do with you, and I hope I never see you again."

As I was about to walk out, he grabbed me by the arm and said, "Please, hear me out. Listen… When economic relationships are free of regulations, everything prospers. Deregulation makes everything easier to manage. This also applies to relationships like ours. You are fucking up our relationship by putting upon it too many rules that chain us. It's in your hands to set us free!"

"Oh. My God! You are so romantic that you can only think of me as an unregulated economy! What's wrong with you? Do the words 'human being' mean anything to you?"

"Stay with me, even if I'm married. Who cares? STOP BEING SO SELF-RIGHTEOUS!"

"SELF-RIGHTEOUS?" I said. "Then why do you go to church every Sunday?"

"I'm an investment banker. I make money everywhere. I make so much money with my contacts at church that if Jesus shows up and finds out how much money I make, he will ask me for his cut! I don't care about what people think of me! That's who I am."

"No! That's not who you are honey! You are a delusional, misogynistic, xenophobic, paranoid, narcissist in need of a ton of massive medication! How did I miss this? Like a fool, I refused to believe the truth about you. So, on behalf of all the women you have used like toilet paper, like your wife, your daughter, and me…!" I threw the drink in his face and walked out of the bar.

As I was walking away down the street, I heard Michael yelling, "BYE *COLUMBIA*. I STILL LOVE YOU *COLUMBIA*!"

I turned in surprise and said, "What? What? What did you just say? Where did you get that? Answer me. Where did you get that? Why did you call me '*Columbia*'? ANSWER ME! Goddammit!"

He responded, "I'm the President of the Condo Board where your *Super* works, that spick fuck. He has made my life impossible for years with his union bullshit. I sent him to therapy because his union insisted. I knew that he went where you work. I asked him for the name of his therapist, and he said, mocking me, "I call her '*Columbia*.' I checked. You're the only one in that place who went to Columbia."

"Listen to me. You don't know what you are doing. You are playing with fire. Stay away from him! This is between you and me. It has nothing to do with him."

"Sorry honey," he said, tilting his head and shrugging his shoulders, "but the ball is rolling."

"What do you mean?"

"The therapy failed. You were my girlfriend, and that's a conflict of interest for you. Therefore, your judgment is compromised. Don't think I'm doing this to coerce you to be with me, but I hope you reconsider."

"Stay away from him." I said. "I'm warning you. Stay away from him!" I began walking away.

He followed me and announced, "Stay with me, and all this will disappear".

I ignored him, and then he had the nerve to yell, "COME BACK! I FORGIVE YOU!"

It is interesting, the damage that two testicles and wealth can do to the psyche of a human being. Hate helped me to get home that night, the same hate that still eats my insides one year later. The next day was going to be my last session with *Super*. I should have tried to focus on the case as much as I could that night, but I couldn't. I prayed all night to God to help *Super,* and me.

# CHAPTER FOURTEEN
## *The Last Session*

I was in my office an hour before my last session. There I was, bumping into chairs and my desk as I walked around the room thinking about how to proceed in the session. My focus wasn't there that day. Perhaps Joe was right when he told me that I was more out of focus than a film student at NYU.

I didn't sleep at all the previous night. I was too preoccupied regarding what to do about my pregnancy. I kept not thinking about why I got pregnant, but rather about why I had to be Catholic. I blamed being Catholic for making me feel super-guilty both about my pregnancy, and the mess involving Michael and *Super*. So, I entirely gave up on trying to sleep. It was impossible at that point.

The new scenario concerning the relationship between my ex-boyfriend and *Super* created a potential ethical conflict of interest that had to be explained, even though I had no knowledge of it until the previous evening. I recognized the possibility that I could lose my license. More immediate, and even more troubling to me, was the problem of my last session with *Super*. It was an issue that had to be explained to Joe if I was to continue with this case. Furthermore, I had new information that I couldn't divulge to *Super*, but that was vital for his employment. Not only could it negatively affect his employment, but also his psychological well-being.

Making matters worse, I felt I could not trust my boss. I had the feeling that all this time he was talking to my mother about me – kissing

93

her ass – to accumulate more points with her for more funding. I was afraid that I would have no other option but to let my mother know that I was pregnant, before Joe told her. Why did I tell him that? Now I remember, because I was afraid that he was going to fire me that day, and I needed him to understand that I had reasons for being unbalanced, and that I was working on it.

But that was then. He needed to keep his mouth shut. I found myself in a dilemma in which I couldn't be truthful with my boss, even though that left me on a potentially unethical route.

I wouldn't have minded only having intakes to do. I now understood the phrase, 'be careful what you wish for because you may get it.' And boy did I get it!

I needed to keep busy finding answers, so I decided to read *Super's* file, and I noticed that he had mentioned that he had a BA in political science, but never mentioned what college he attended. He was definitely well educated, so I had no doubt that he went to college. Perhaps the intake interview was not properly conducted; he simply wasn't asked about the college he attended. That is something I might want to explore. But at that moment it seemed so irrelevant within the new context of the case that I brushed it aside.

I was feeling that everything surrounding me began spinning around in my head: the nonprofit, my boss, my ex-boyfriend, and my mother were all conspiring to destroy either *Super,* or me, or perhaps both. I didn't know what to do. I had no answers. The night before I had prayed and prayed. My anger was able to sneak these words into my prayer, "Thank you God for not listening. When I die, if you ask me about my life,

I would like to have a small dispensation from you to be allowed to ask you about this shitty night and where the hell you were?"

I didn't know what to do. I was feeling even more distraught than during the previous night. Then I heard the door opening. *Super* entered. He had a little grin on his lips. I instinctively smiled, a smile that was like asking myself, "What the hell is going on?"

Then, without saying a word, he pointed at the chair.

I immediately tried to apologize before he complained about the chair, "I'm sorry they haven't..."

He interrupted me, "I know. I know. Don't worry."

"What the hell was going on?" I wondered.

He said, "Don't worry."

Maybe God was listening after all. At that moment I decided to tell *Super* about the conversation between Michael and myself; the conversation about his employment, as devastating as all of that was. A whole night of thinking about how to tell him the bad news, and in the end, I improvised, "*Super*, I would like to have a word with you."

"I will have a word with you if you keep your word to use only one word!"

Surprised, I said, "Why are you so funny today? Listen, your file doesn't say what college you attended."

"I graduated from Columbia University... Political Science, Class of 1981."

I couldn't believe it. "WHAT? WHAT? YOU GRADUATED FROM COLUMBIA? AND YOU PUT ME THROUGH THIS 'COLUMBIA' BULLSHIT FOR FOUR SESSIONS?"

"Yes. I got a bunch of scholarships, but I always felt like an outsider. But I made it. By the way, the story of deciding between law school and the baby is totally true."

He had played me from the beginning. I was more furious than I was with Michael the night before, and that is a mouthful. I said to him, "I can't believe that I'm about to become the first therapist that kills her client during therapy!"

I kept walking around the office trying to gain some composure, but he was different from the previous four sessions; he wasn't uptight or in a bad mood. He was looking at me as if he was mocking me, and having fun while doing it. He was completely relaxed.

I said, "Anyway, you seem to be in a better mood today. What is going on?"

"My daughter and my granddaughter are coming to visit me in three days. They are going to stay for a week! And after we finish our last session today, my job will be secure again."

I felt like the rain clouds and winds had dissipated after an all-night hurricane. I felt immediate relief. I was finally free to let my guard down and let him feel that he was talking to another person, not a therapist, "Oh. That's great news! I am so happy for you. Since you are in such a good mood, I want to try something different. I want to ask you. What do you do in your time off?"

"Movies. I like the darkness in the theater where you can only see shadows of people who don't want to be seen, like beings in a cave sitting in obscurity, like comrades wanting to see something on the screen that they are not."

"You describe it like a meditation. Have you ever meditated?"

"*Columbia*, supers don't meditate. We decided that in a union meeting a long time ago."

"Well, since you mentioned movies," I said, "let me try something here. Let's make a movie of the life you wish to have. You start".

"Ok. What if I had become a lawyer? How successful could I have been? My wife and child would have been able to live in a better home."

"Please, bear with me," I said. "Forget this is a therapy session. I want you to imagine getting back at all those Westsiders and Eastsiders who treated you like shit for all these years."

*Super* tensed up his arms in a show of enthusiasm and said, "*COLUMBIA*, LET'S DO THERAPY!"

"Just let your mind be free and listen. You go back and finish law school. Then you will enjoy viewing all those people dropping their jaws when they see you with your briefcase ready to sue them."

"Oh," said *Super* with a playful look, "please don't stop now!"

"OK, let's see... Oh! You will sue them for all the anti-labor practices that saved them hundreds of thousands of dollars."

*Super* had a big grin when he said, "That sounds good. Keep going!"

"The newspapers will write on the first page, "Former super becomes a lawyer at the age of sixty, and makes millions suing former employers."

"Now we're talking. Don't stop!" he said.

"Oh, you are going to like this one. And now your ex-wife... When she finds out about your success, she tries to get back with you, and you tell her to go fuck herself!"

"THIS IS HOW YOU DO THERAPY *COLUMBIA*!" said *Super* as he gave a little fist pump.

"Am I getting better?"

"Yes, I think the Columbia therapy professors would be amazed if they came here and saw how suicidal people like me can help their fucked-up alumni!"

Then Joe opened the door and, sticking his head in, asked, "Why is this happening again?"

*Super* slid the chair toward Joe and said, "Fuck off, and take this fucking chair with you!"

Joe was so scared that he left without closing the door.

I didn't want to work there anymore, and said to *Super,* "I am so fired! Ah! I don't care anymore. I'm resigning and going to work in another place, you see. You see!"

*Super* responded, "I see what?"

"For the first time. I see you smiling," I said.

"I would make one correction to the story you just made up."

"What would you change?"

*Super* said, "I would have taken my wife back."

"Really?" I said. "Would you forgive her?"

"In a second!"

"How do you know that you still love her?"

98

"You are in love when you still feel the first kiss you gave to someone years later. That's what I feel when I think of my wife."

"I hope one day someone will feel that way about me."

"Hey! I'm concerned about you. I'm a father. I know when something is wrong. What's happening?"

"I'm not immune just because I happen to be a therapist," I said.

"The five sessions are over," he replied. "You are not my therapist anymore. What is it? A guy?"

"Yes."

"He betrayed you too?"

"Yes."

"Are you married?"

"No. He is."

"*Columbia!*"

"I didn't know! He lied to me!"

"That's fine, as long as you don't get pregnant."

I noticed *Super* approaching me, and I feared the intimacy of his coming closer. Then I found myself grabbing his hands, and he said, "Sweetheart, are you pregnant?"

"Sorry. I shouldn't have touched you! It was unprofessional."

"Forget that. I told you, the sessions are over. What are you going to do about the pregnancy?"

"You know I'm Catholic."

"Did you know Catholics are originally from the West Side?"

"I shouldn't be in this profession trying to help people when the one who needs help is me!"

"What are you going to do about the pregnancy?" he asked again.

"I can't be a mother now. I just can't."

"Do your parents know?"

"They don't know. My father is a big developer. He spends his time drinking scotch and playing golf all day. My mother runs a multi-million-dollar family foundation that she inherited, but she doesn't really care about. She medicates herself with painkillers and spends most of her time buying crap she doesn't need at Bloomingdales. The truth is that my mother goes to Bloomingdales to cry, but she doesn't know it. Sad, isn't it? My supervisor wants me here, not because he thinks I'm a good therapist, but because he wants my mother's money. One of the things I regret the most in my life is that I have never had a meaningful conversation with any person of color. My interactions have consisted basically of 'yes,' 'please,' 'excuse me,' 'thanks,' 'you're welcome,' and some extra trivial pleasantries, but never deep enough to really develop a friendship. And then you came. What a fucking roller coaster of a revelation you have been for me! I tried to pretend as much as I could that your comments weren't affecting me. You really did a fucking job on me. Still, I always liked you. I was sure that deep down you never wanted to hurt me. I have lived surrounded by all of these worlds, and yet I couldn't see you well. I failed as a therapist."

"*Columbia*, please listen. Listen carefully. Because of the therapy, I called my daughter and asked her to come. You kept your word. I feel better now. I hope it lasts. You are a good human being."

"That means a lot to me. Listen, after all these sessions, something is very clear to me. You need a big change at work. Please trust me on this one. Find a new building to work. Please, it's not good for you"

"I don't understand," said *Super*, looking confused. "I'm used to that building. I'm too old to be changing buildings."

I took a deep breath and said, "Just think about it." Then I dared to say the most unprofessional thing a clinician could say, "Can we get together and talk once in a while?"

"Why not?" he answered, and continued, "I don't want this just to be a vague promise. Let's get together before my daughter comes. Is that ok?"

"That would be unprofessional of me, but I'm not good at following rules, so it's OK!" I said as *Super* headed toward the door.

He turned back and said, "Listen, when we go out to talk, you pay!"

"OK. Bye, *Super*."

Right after I said those words, he looked at me without saying anything. I saw his face turn regretful, like he had a premonition that something was wrong, or missing in the conversation. Then he lowered his head and said, "Bye, *Columbia*." He turned toward the door and left without looking back.

I was happy for *Super,* but still knew that much worse news was about to come to him. That's why I accepted the invitation to see him one more time in a less conventional manner. I knew that even when I was no longer his therapist, ethical rules forbade me from making non-therapeutic appointments with him, particularly right after I closed his case. However,

I couldn't imagine the idea that I wouldn't be there for him, especially since it was my ex-boyfriend who was about to turn his life upside down.

I also had to make a decision about having this baby. I didn't think I was ready psychologically to be a good mother. I believed I had to leave everything behind as soon as possible and get out of New York. I decided to resign the next day. The hell with my mother and Joe!

## CHAPTER FIFTEEN
### *Super and the Ex-Boyfriend*

The next morning, *Super* went to work. I can only imagine that he spent the whole day thinking of his daughter and granddaughter who were arriving in two days to be with him. His work, as busy as always, went by that day as easily as a pigeon floating on a sunny day over Central Park.

He worked on automatic, doing all he had to do while dreaming of a near future when he would finally be communicating easily with his daughter and granddaughter, and traveling to California once in a while to spend time with them.

As the Palmieri music was blasting in his earphones, he imagined that he was dancing salsa with his granddaughter the same way he did with his daughter when she was a child and the whole family was together in his apartment. He thought about hugging his granddaughter and daughter, kissing them, and laughing with them. I am sure he thought about all that as he mopped a floor, made plumbing repairs, swept the hallway and the sweat from his forehead.

He didn't notice that he was working because he was dreaming of a new beginning. As he used to say, '*Work is not a problem.*' It was clear to me that for him work was easier when he had the love of his family. It was his soul that needed work, and the physical movement to defeat the stagnation of feelings that had paralyzed him during the last few years. Joe was right that he might be a political activist, but even an activist needs a family. For them, their families are also part of the community, and they need both.

And there he was, dancing as he mopped the hallway floor when the elevator door opened, and Michael quickly walked out holding an envelope in his right hand and shaking it against his thigh as he smiled. He turned towards *Super* and yelled at him, "Hey, SUPER! HEY, TAKE OFF THE EARPHONES!"

*Super* responded, "What are you saying? Wait a second!" as he took his earphones off.

Michael continued, "Here, you are fired!  A check is inside. Bye."

*Super* look at the envelope, "What?"

"Wasn't I clear?" said Michael. "You are fired. Get the fuck out."

"What's wrong?" said *Super* in a tone matching Michael's aggression, with added sarcasm, "You couldn't find your suppositories this morning?" *Super* finished reading the letter and said, "I have a union, and you don't have cause to fire me. The Labor Board won't accept this either!"

"Fuck you," said Michael, "fuck the union, and fuck the Labor Board. The only Board that counts is the Condo's Board, which I chair. I want you out! Get the fuck out, or I'll call the police."

"Why are you doing this?" asked the *Super*.

Michael gave him a look and said, "You are mentally ill. Loco en la cabeza."

"You, ignorant prick!" *Super* shot back. "Haven't you read the news?  In what fucking bubble do you live? Half the country is mentally ill!"

"*Columbia*," replied Michael, "that's what you call my girlfriend? Remember? Well, I can't believe she is your therapist."

CHAPTER FIFTEEN

"*Columbia?!*" *Super* yelled, disoriented, "*Columbia!?*" *Super's* heart froze. I wonder if – like me – when the pain in his soul was so deep, a series of thoughts travelled toward his brain in less than a second, computing a new reality that was then encapsulated there: my betrayal, the economic danger of losing his job, unemployment, poverty, perhaps homelessness, and his pride – which was his most treasured commodity. Yes, I bet he thought of all of that in a second. *Super* responded with a whisper from deep down his soul, "No, it can't be! She is with you?"

"Yes," said Michael. "She is my girlfriend."

*Super* blinked and asked, "Did she talk to you about me?"

"Yes, and she told me everything about your case. Everything. – She thinks you wasted her time."

"She would never say that," said *Super*, in a somber tone.

"Are you fucking kidding me?" said Michael with a little chuckle. "Come on! I thought you at least had a brain. You're a lab rat for her! You are her first case ever. Maybe I will reconsider a letter of recommendation."

"I bet you feel very powerful right now," said *Super*.

"I always do. Why?" asked Michael, casually.

"Because it's always easy to feel tall in obscurity! And you are full of darkness."

"*Super*, let me give you some advice from the bottom of my heart, and I really mean this, because you are really good people. Listen, I think it's time for you to jump from a fucking window. You will be doing yourself and all of us a big fucking favor!" Michael left.

Later that night I was in the office debating with myself. Since my last session with *Super*, I had increasingly become more fearful for his future, especially if Michael kept his promise to fire him. I could only hope that he was bluffing. I felt responsible for what might happen, but I couldn't prevent it from happening.

I think you can see by now how insecure I had become. I wasn't like this until I started working as a therapist. But I couldn't diagnose myself, and I didn't know of a therapist who could give me an immediate appointment and advise me through these uncertainties. I definitely couldn't tell Joe. That had been out of the question for a while.

Then Joe came to my office without knocking – this was his custom. He didn't say hello. He seemed to be upset, and said, "The union and the insurance agreed on five more visits for *Super*. I need you to transfer the case to administration."

"When did you get the insurance approval?" I asked.

"Last week."

I was furious. "Last fucking week? Why didn't you tell me then?"

"Yesterday both of you told me to 'fuck off'. That's evidence that you lost control of the case. I told your mother. She made me promise that you wouldn't see him again."

All I could say was, "FUCK YOU AND MY MOTHER TOO! You can't play with people's lives like that!"

Joe calmly stated, "He was taking advantage of you."

"That's not true!" I said. "There are other issues. He will lose his job, and his apartment, but he doesn't know that yet. So, he still needs to come to see me!"

"How do you know that? Have you been hiding information from me? Anyway, your mother will talk to you later."

Joe left like a typical man – slamming the door.

The telephone rang immediately. It was Michael. I answered, "What are you doing calling me? I told you to stay away from me! What? You fired him? …You mentioned me? …You have no idea what you have done!" I hung up.

Once again, multiple thoughts per second began invading my brain: '*Where is Super now? Is he depressed? Is he blaming me?*' I thought that tomorrow, I should reach out to him. '*What if he doesn't answer my call? Should I go to his home and talk to him personally?*' I was feeling so much hate for Michael and Joe and my mother that my reading glasses wanted to escape from my face.

I had to go to *Super's* home NOW.

# CHAPTER SIXTEEN
## *The Window*

*Super* arrived at his apartment bruised by the encounter with Michael, but not completely depressed. Perhaps he was buoyed by the fact that his expulsion wasn't totally complete, since the union hadn't responded yet. His years of experience as a union representative gave him some hope of prevailing. He had definitely finished his five sessions as agreed between the union and the condo board, and he was sure that my report was going to state that he could continue to work.

Besides all that, the expectation of seeing his daughter and granddaughter in a couple of days superseded everything. The timing of his daughter's visit was perfect.

My mind, on the other hand, kept operating like a swing in a children's park, moving my thoughts back and forth, back and forth. Only the remaining bit of professional discipline left in me acted as a shield that prevented me from feeling completely lost.

When *Super* entered his apartment and closed the door behind him, he saw an envelope under the door. It was from one of Michael's real estate investment companies.

Michael had told me the truth when he remarked that he bought *Super's* building and was evicting the tenants. I really don't think he did that to get back at me. I truly believe his motivation was more that he saw it as a good investment opportunity. For Michael, a good deal was always more important than retribution. Like the good opportunist that he was, Michael understood that emotions are put aside when business

109

demands. Money shone above everything, even love or hate. I guess that he just found the property a desirable business investment, and that was all. But that's just my guess.

The reality was that Michael now had possession. The fact that *Super* was in his cross hairs just made him accelerate his actions a bit. His plan was to renovate and sell the apartments as condos, but first he had to evict all the rental tenants. That scenario was going to be devastating for *Super,* and many other families. A proud man who was about to lose his home of thirty years due to a simple numerical Wall Street transaction.

People like *Super* have strong principles. People that Michael generally dealt with devour principled people. They are just as cold as the numbers on the spreadsheets that increase their wealth. After the deal is done in their offices, they celebrate in a bar with their mistresses and/or call girls. The next office day, they go at it again.

When *Super* saw the letter on the floor he bent slowly. A result of a whole day of mopping, sweeping, and repairing plumbing; feeling the back pain caused by forty years of work. It now felt as if he were carrying 40 pounds of bricks on his back. He grabbed the envelope. Then he tried to stand firmly, expending the same amount of energy, and feeling the pain that almost prevented him from bending down in the first place. He walked slowly to his chair, like a lost man who had just recognized the fragility of the props of his world.

Generally, once he closed his apartment door behind him, the outside world was a desert, and the inside was his oasis. There, inside, is where he walked shoeless on his old dusty rug as if he were on a sandy beach. He drank a glass of water as if it were a coconut and sat down in his chair as if it were under a palm tree. Then he exhaled the whole day of work through his mouth while closing his eyes in relief.

Not that day. There he was sitting, ready to read the letter. As he read it, he read in disbelief. He read it again and again. He read not only every sentence of the eviction notice, but also read his whole fucked-up day like the afternoon edition of the newspaper that informed the entire City of the breaking news that he was fucked – destroyed!

Yes, after that day, which insisted on not being over yet, he spoke out loud as if he was complaining to Gods that he didn't believe in. But if they happened to exist, they were definitely complicit in destroying his life. "They sold the building. They sold it! They are throwing me out of the apartment after thirty years. I got gentrified up the ass."

Then the telephone rang, and he answered. It was his daughter. "Hi sweetheart. How are you?"

Meanwhile, I was in the office looking frantically for *Super's* address in the file. The file wasn't where I expected, so I tried to look through my notes to find his address and telephone number. No luck. I ran to my desk and slipped on the floor while bending toward the lowest drawer. In there I did find his file, while tears cascaded out of my eyes, blinding me temporarily. I finally got his address and phone number and called *Super*. "Pick it up, pick up! Damn it! – Fuck me!"

His telephone was busy. I left the office running and grabbed a taxi. He lived not that far away from the office, but I couldn't manage to run over there. I had had cramps all day and was spotting occasionally. I meant to go to the gynecologist, but I had been so worried about the dealings between Michael and *Super* that I neglected to make an appointment.

Meanwhile, *Super* was talking to his daughter on the telephone. "You can't come? Why? – You are going where? – She is getting married... I didn't – But I don't want you to go. – Why are you going? – Where? – Sweetheart! After what she did to us? – Can you promise me that you will think about it? Please, I beg you. – I miss you so much. – Remember, you are my universe. You are all – Are you happy? – Listen, you are right. You should go to your mother's wedding. Remember this, please. You must remember this. – I will be with you even if you can't hear me or see me. Always! – Everything is fine. – I love you too."

He hung up.

It was already dark and cloudy. Fall was almost over, and people were feeling a slight chill of winter. I had left my coat at the office. I arrived at *Super's* apartment in less than 15 minutes. *Super* lived on the 12th floor. People hanging around in the lobby area looked at me as if I didn't belong, and I agreed with them. I definitely didn't belong. I pressed the elevator button, but the elevator didn't respond, so I waited for almost five minutes. A young man yelled that the elevator wasn't working.

So, I took the stairs. After the 5th floor I felt that I was spotting more than before, but I couldn't stop there. It was dark. I heard young people running down the stairs and yelling until they came to me. They asked me if I was lost. One of them asked me if I needed help. I said I was OK. Then he said, "Be careful. I don't think you should be in the stairway with all that jewelry and expensive clothing."

I answered, "The elevator is not working."

112

He said, "We know that." And he kept going with the rest of the group.

Inside the apartment *Super* was walking in circles. Then he stopped and began banging his head slowly against the wall. It seemed he was punishing himself for everything that was happening, but perhaps the fact that he couldn't punish those who put him in that position was the cause. I think *Super* wanted to punish someone, and there was no one else in the world left to punish but him.

*Super* pulled a photo of his daughter from his pocket. He stopped next to his desk and wrote a note explaining the moments since he had come into the apartment, as well as the rest of the day. I still wonder why he wrote it. Was it for me? Was it perhaps because of my suggestion that he use writing in order to release tension and reflect? Or was it because he wanted to explain his suicide to his daughter? I gathered from the letter that he was suffocating and had taken a long breath and fell on his knees gasping for air.

He put the letter in an envelope and left it on the desk. Then he stood up and walked slowly toward the window and opened it.

I finally reached his apartment and pushed the door and – thank God – it was still unlatched and unlocked. I was completely out of breath. I wanted to talk, but I thought that if I opened my mouth, I might vomit. Instead of really speaking, I managed to whisper, "Hi."

*Super* turned, surprised that I was there. "What the fuck are you doing here?"

I said, "The elevator wasn't working. I walked twelve floors to get here."

He said sarcastically, "The elevators had a union meeting and decided not to go up anymore."

I was so happy to hear him joking. Then I noticed that he was near the open window. It was chilly outside. "Why was that window open?" I thought. Alarmed, I exclaimed, "Please! Move away from the window. Please, move. Move!"

He didn't say anything, but he kept staring at me with such rage that for the first time I felt afraid of him.

I said, "So, I got more sessions from the insurance. Like a hundred, you won't believe how many I got."

"You betrayed me!" he said. "You spoke to your boyfriend about me, and he fucked me. You fucked me! I knew I couldn't trust you!"

"No! I didn't know you work in his building. I swear! He connected the dots when you mentioned 'Columbia' to him. I would have never betrayed you. You know that!"

He looked at me with a blank face. "You're a fucking hypocrite. A hypocrite!"

"He lied to you!" I pleaded. "He lied to you! Why do you think I'm here? Think about it. Why am I here?"

"I got gentrified. I lost my job. I have lost everything in one day. My daughter... my daughter cancelled. She has to go to her mother's wedding. Fucking walls!"

I talked softly, "Just come from the window. We have a date, did you forget? Let's get out of here. Please!"

Suddenly I had strong pain in my stomach and legs and fell on my knees. He asked, "What happened? Are you OK?" And he came and grabbed me.

"No," I said, wincing. "It is nothing, just a cramp in my legs. The stairs were too much."

"You are pregnant. You shouldn't have walked up here." He was so tender.

I said, "Since when do you care?"

He didn't respond. He kept holding me like no one had held me before. He was so paternal; he kept holding me until suddenly I felt uncomfortable that anyone would care about me in such fashion, especially after what I did – even if it was unintentional. I felt that I didn't deserve his concern for my health. So, I said, "I'm OK now. Let me go! Don't worry about me! Let go of me!" But he wouldn't let go of me. "I swear I'm OK. I'm OK!"

I got up. I knew that I needed him to get out of the apartment and close the damn window. I said, "Let's get out of here. Please! You can't give up now."

He sighed. "I have nothing to show for the sweat of my years – not even a family or a home. I don't want anyone to think I'm a coward. I'm not a fucking coward. You understand me? It is just that life has never made sense to me. Why is it wrong to die on your own terms?"

I said very seriously, "This is not you. I know. It's not you. You will get out of this by letting your heart lead you out of it."

"What are you talking about, *Columbia*? Don't you fucking get it?"

"Not tonight! Not tonight. Please. Not tonight." I pleaded with him.

Then he seemed to come to his senses and said, "What am I talking about? I'm sorry. You are right! Let's get out of here. I want to talk to you about those extra sessions. Let's go! You go first. Go ahead."

I was so happy that he listened to me and wanted to leave the apartment, so I excitedly started talking. "Great. Next week you can start with a different therapist if you wish, and we will..."

At that moment we had arrived at the door. He put his arm around me from behind and opened the door as I was talking. Then *Super* grabbed me by the arm and pushed me gently outside the apartment and locked the door behind me. And he said, "There you go!"

I found myself out of the apartment trying to open the door. "SUPER? SUPER, OPEN THE FUCKING DOOR NOW! OPEN IT! OPEN THE DOOR, PLEASE! OPEN THE FUCKING DOOR!"

He yelled through the door, "*COLUMBIA*, PLEASE LISTEN. JUST LISTEN."

I stopped yelling, and said from the other side of the door, "OK, tell me. Please talk to me."

"My hate is not enough to survive in this city. Go home please."

I started yelling again, "I'M NOT LEAVING UNTIL YOU OPEN THIS FUCKING DOOR! PLEASE LET ME IN. LET ME IN." I kept pushing the door as hard as I could.

"Do you remember what I told you about Masada?" he asked.

"Yes!"

"In New York, buildings are mountains. Well, I'm going to die in my mountain. This is my mountain."

I kept pushing the door, and I noticed that the old door was giving in. I just had to keep talking to him.

Now he was yelling. "I'M GOING TO DIE IN MY MOUNTAIN. THIS IS MY MOUNTAIN! THIS IS MY LIFE!"

"OPEN THE DOOR!" I screamed back. "PLEASE! OPEN THE FUCKING DOOR! OPEN! OPEN THE FUCKING DOOR."

By that time the tenants were all in the hallway. The teenagers that I spoke on the stairs were there too. Specifically, the kid that spoke to me on the stairs whispered in my ear that the neighbors had already called the police.

Then *Super* yelled as he walked away from the door and towards the window, "DO YOU REMEMBER WHAT I TOLD YOU IN OUR FIRST SESSION ABOUT FUCKING FAULKNER?"

"NO PLEASE TELL ME AGAIN. I DON'T REMEMBER. I CAN BARELY HEAR YOU. CAN YOU COME CLOSER TO THE DOOR? I CAN'T HEAR YOU WELL."

Then the teenager began pushing the door with me.

*Super* said, "I'D RATHER DIE THAN BE WHIPPED. – FUCKING CITY. FUCK YOU FAULKNER. – FUCKING CITY, YOU GAVE ME NOTHING. YOU HEAR ME?! YOU GAVE ME NOTHING!"

"GODDAMNIT!" I yelled. "OPEN THE FUCKING DOOR! OPEN IT!"

I could hear him yelling on the other side of the apartment. "I GAVE YOU. I GAVE YOU. HEY, NEW YORK! YOU TOOK MY HOME. YOU TOOK MY JOB, MY FAMILY. YOU TOOK MY DIGNITY. YOU TOOK MY SANITY, YOU MOTHERFUCKERS! YOU GAVE ME NOTHING. – I GAVE YOU. I GAVE YOU! – WHAT A BEAUTIFUL NIGHT!!!! – BY THE WAY, GOD, GO TO HELL TOO!"

I heard the sound of traffic through the door, and I thought that he might be on the window ledge already. The door finally gave in. I ran to the middle of the living room. I fell. He was already standing on the ledge outside the window.

He said, "FINALLY!"

He jumped.

I heard from the living room when his body hit the street. The same street that he once told me he used to walk at night, 'trying to find a piece of pavement to cheer me up.' There on that same cement there were people screaming; sounds of shoes pounding the street toward or away from his body; cars suddenly stopping and crashing into each other; cars honking; voices asking, "Who was that?" "From where?" "He jumped from up there?" "How?" "Oh my God!" "Is it the super?" "*Super*? NOOO. It can't be!" "Who? *Super*?" "He jumped from where? No!" "Impossible. It can't be him." "My God, oh my God. Look at him. Look at him!" "No!"

I couldn't move. Those street voices were giving me other meanings for the words spoken like, 'Do not move. The whole world ended out there. Stay here.'

The window curtain was dancing with the breeze entering the apartment, waving at me as if it was inviting me to join *Super* and jump. I closed my eyes looking for an old nightmare even worse than the one that I was living – a nightmare that would suddenly wake me up. But it wasn't there. What was happening was true. It was reality.

A woman neighbor came running in and closed the window. Another grabbed me and took me outside the apartment. They were both crying and terrified. Still, they had the decency to care for me. I thanked them and told them that I had to go. They asked me what happened. I said, "He jumped."

Then they asked me, "Why? What did you do to him?"

"Nothing... I came to stop him." I don't know if they believed me.

I left the same way I came in. Every step walking down the stairs felt as if I were pressing my feet against my own heart. Every step felt like death. The stairs began moving like a spiral hypnotizing me. I didn't know where I was or where I was going, but wherever I was going, my legs didn't want to follow. I just knew that I had to keep pushing my feet to get down, to ask *Super*, 'Why?'

'Why?' became my goal. 'Why?' was my reason to live, to walk down that labyrinth. 'Why?' was my savior. 'Why?' was my light at the end of the spiral stairs. 'Why?' here – and then at the bottom floor – 'Why?' again. 'Why?' took me out of the building, blinded by the blue and red lights of the police cars and ambulances outside coming through the glass of the lobby area.

The sounds – the sounds, those fucking sounds of desperation and horror from people, mixed with the smell of winter falling on the City, intruding into the darkness of the night. Suddenly, I asked myself, "Why am I here? Oh my God I am pregnant. I am bleeding. Why? What's happening? I am diseased!" Then I saw a blanket, red and white, on the ground with boots stained with red. I asked myself, "What is that?"

I walked over to it, and a policeman stopped me with his hand saying, "Ma'am, you can't go there. Please step back."

I bent under his arm to get a better view. "Oh my God, it's *Super*!" I said to myself. The red on the white blanket was his blood. I woke up and screamed, "No! Why? Why? Why?"

The policeman asked if I knew him.

"Yes."

He pulled me aside on the sidewalk and told me to wait there. I waited, paralyzed while feeling myself dripping warm drops of blood all over my thighs. But I didn't care. Maybe that was the best thing that could have happened to me that night.

I looked around and hundreds of people were surrounding the area. As he lay in the middle of El Barrio, the streets wobbled like a vacillating flame announcing the news of his death as though it were an earthquake. The windows in El Barrio began to light up in hundreds of what *Super* called 'mountains.' From the 'mountains,' one 'mountain' after another, people ran out into the street. He died in the North, South, East, and West of the neighborhood. El Barrio lit up in debt to him. El Barrio was in pain.

Candles appeared on the streets of every corner of the neighborhood, illuminating their sadness. Flowers and tears surrounded the streets. People were yelling "El *Super* is dead – El *Super* is dead – El

*Super* murio!" A rainbow of people of all colors: brown, black, and white Latinos descended on the street, illuminating the darkness of the night.

Puerto Ricans brought their flags and laid them on top of the now red blanket that covered his body. Dominicans, Colombians, Mexicans, and Blacks were on the street too, saying to each other "The brother is dead! The brother is dead, *Super* is dead!" There was pain in New York City, but only East Harlem knew it.

I had never experienced what the death of a hero felt like until I was totally overwhelmed by watching *Super's* people surround him. I saw wide eyes of surprise; closed eyes in prayers; sad eyes of non-believers; eyes looking down with pain; and eyes looking up asking God for answers. The hero wasn't alone. I learned that night that I didn't know anything about that man until I saw his people. Now I know him. I found him in his death.

I stood there, and people began telling stories to each other of his activism during the 70's, 80's, 90's, and as recently as a couple of years ago. Then he had suddenly disappeared from action.

Thirty years ago, he saved the primary care clinic where our mental health program was located from being closed due to lack of governmental funding. Ironically, he saved the job I held; he saved the place where we met, at least that's what I like to believe now that I'm writing this history.

He also organized thousands of tenants in the seven public housing complexes known as 'the projects' to demand immediate renovations, including new boilers, before winter from the Housing and Urban Development (HUD) agency.

Thousands of families were therefore able to survive the New York winter comfortably. And he didn't even live in 'the projects.' I heard about when he was in his early twenties and he took over the main offices of the Metropolitan Hospital with dozens of other activists to demand better quality and greater access to health care for poor people. He was also one of the students that took over the office of the President of Columbia University during the student strike of 1970.

He never told me about it, but many people talked mostly about his arduous defense and advocacy for the independence of Puerto Rico, and an end to its colonial status. From the 70's onward he testified at the United Nations on that issue as a member of the Puerto Rican Socialist Party.

He was also incarcerated for civil disobedience many times for each one of those issues.

An unsung hero known for defending his community who was not documented sufficiently in writing, he was recognized in the oral tradition of his followers. A woman said that doing his type of activist work also creates a lot of enemies. Enemies that sometimes you don't even know you have. A man responded to her by wondering if he was pushed through the window.

The 'gentrifiers' that were walking in the area appeared to be repulsed by the scene. They moved away with the same disdain that they exhibited for people like *Super* every day. They were not interested in knowing who he was. It turned out I was the only white person interested – not only because I was his therapist, but because I wanted to know more about him even after his death. Standing there, I realized that this was the sixth session, but this time it wasn't about him, but about me knowing him in his totality. His death became my therapist.

Whatever I thought I knew about the City was wrong. I didn't know the whole of the City until I saw him dead on the street. God bless him and condemn my blindness.

Now I know all his sacrifices and struggles, victories and defeats as an activist and organizer. He never let me know about what a big deal his activism was, or even what he did through the years. And there he was, lying on the pavement, telling me – yelling at me, "Look at me, look at me, look at me!"

*Super* loved humanity, and in the end, due to his pride, all he had was a 24-year-old naive girl from the West Side trying to help him, and not knowing how. The irony is that everything he fought against was embodied in me. No wonder he made me work so hard at the beginning of our sessions. Still, all he had for me in the end was love because he couldn't stop loving. He closed the apartment door and left me outside to protect me from his jumping through the window. Real love loves everything; not one, but all. He was love even when he was angry. I'm so proud to have known him, and to be with someone like him in his most difficult and last moment on earth.

He had only himself, his courage and his people – no money or political connections in his favor, and he was still a winner that the City hid from the rest of us for decades. As Joe said once, "When you don't like something, just change the channel." I wonder if that's why *Super* cursed the City before he jumped. How can a city know nothing about such a giant?

Perhaps it is because we weren't told to look. But even if we had been told to look, we would have continued to look the other way anyway.

We can be murderous in so many ways oblivious to us. Instead of killing them with one shot, we whip them slowly, drop by drop, until we displace them from their lands, like Custer did with Native Americans, and like Romans did with the Masada Jews. Until ... one day they die from a self-inflicted wound from the sword of their pride. They prefer to be killed than to be whipped. Pride is what keeps you alive, and pride can make you die. When their mountains are surrounded, proud people fight back until they decide that death, just like life, belongs to them – not to God.

I realized through these months of reflecting on his death that there was no difference between *Super's* death and his mother's death, even though she died of a heart attack in the police precinct, after striking the garment company. They died of the same thing. They were disposable. I think that's how he felt that night after losing his job and his apartment. I guess he saw it coming for a long time. Loneliness increases with time, I guess. He had no place to go. All the exits were closed, and he was tired of it all, up there on the 12th floor of his mountain. Who am I to judge him?

And there was *Super*, laying 'on the street made of vulgarity' as he once called it in one of our sessions – laying on it as a working man that was thrown out of a window. Michael killed him; the 'gentrifiers' killed him; this fucking City killed him; and me too. He knew he was never going to lose his daughter's love for him. I guess he understood that she needed to fly alone. Sadly, the existential loneliness that kept accelerating towards him also killed him.

124

# CHAPTER SEVENTEEN
## *Super in My Dream*

The police came and interviewed me. The tenants had given testimony that I was trying to help. I told the police that I was *Super's* therapist. Because I had been concerned about him, I went to visit him. I gave them my contact information as well as Joe's. The police let me go.

Those were my last words in days. I became mute – catatonic. I didn't care whether I was pregnant or breathing. I planned to walk back home to the West Side through Central Park at 110th and Lexington. I didn't want to see a doctor. Nothing. I just wanted to be home.

As I entered Central Park in the middle of the night it began to snow. Then, I fell – unconscious. I found out later that the same police officers that had interviewed me later saw me going into the park. Fortunately, they noticed that I wasn't in good shape when I entered the park and decided to follow me. They saw me fall on the ground and called an ambulance. Mount Sinai Hospital was just a couple of blocks away.

There I woke up two days later. A doctor told me that I had lost the baby. I had no reaction. The medical types surrounding my bed asked me for the names of anyone who could take me home. I said that I had nobody. I didn't want my mother to know anything.

Nonetheless, she came to the hospital with Joe the next day. I should have figured that the police would call Joe for verification of my statements after *Super's* suicide. My fucking luck is such that when I woke up that morning the first things, I saw were those two faces. It turned out that my mother had desperately looked for me throughout the City until Joe called her.

Annoyance has nothing on exasperation. My mother was the last thing I wanted to see near me. Thank God that I was medicated with painkillers. They were prescribed because of my injured uterus. I was so thankful for those painkillers, not because they were treating my physical pain, but because without them I wouldn't have been able to deal with my mother. So, from now on, fuck talk therapy; use medication to be able to tolerate your mother.

Now I know that we live with a pathology that will never be taught in psychology class. It isn't always the fault of the individual or genetics or chemical imbalance. I think that we are all fucked up one way or another just by living in this society. Not even writing can mitigate the perversity of death. And still despite that, I decided to write about what happened in those five sessions, and directly afterwards, in order to see if I can make sense of it. Without writing occasionally, I don't know if I would be alive today.

Yes, I am alive, even if not well. I really don't want to kill myself like *Super* did. I am too much of a pathetic coward to do that. Am I experiencing post-traumatic stress disorder? Most likely!

After a year, I still have no contact with my family or Michael. I am living off my trust, which is the only thing for which I thank my parents. I bet *Super* would have said something like, 'trusts – their only purpose is to keep the status quo of the wealthy permanent.' It's clear to me that it's not a good thing for a twenty-five-year-old woman to still be totally dependent on a trust, but that's how it is right now.

Without my parents' wealth and their reputation in the City, I would have been hospitalized in a psychiatric ward, or living homeless on the streets of this 'compassionate' city. Of course, you know I am being sarcastic. What else can you do but be sarcastic, when you are mentally ill?

My father might think that I am still living in the same apartment as my mother. Why not? He never noticed me when I was there. Why should he think otherwise? Regarding my mother, I don't allow her to visit or to have any contact with me. I think that's my way of punishing her and protecting myself from her well-intended meddling in my life. Did you notice that I said, *'well intended'*? That's because I'm working hard to forgive her, but I'm not there yet.

In the past year, Michael has rapidly increased his fortune, and his wife never divorced him. The truth is that she has manipulated him with threats, so that she can continue to play the role of the loving wife. In reality, what both of them want is to look like they are the *crème de la crème* of New York society. Marital loyalty is secondary for them, or perhaps plays no role at all.

As you can see, one should never underestimate the power of hypocrisy as long as it can make you happy. That's why there are so many hypocrites in this world. Hypocrisy works – and the wealthy have a monopoly on it.

I can't forgive Michael for being the trigger that made *Super* kill himself. I count the days until I can allow myself to see Michael again. What would I do? I don't know since I'm not completely stable yet. But what I need is an excuse and opportunity, anything that can help me to make him pay for what he did. I know that opportunity will appear.

I only hope that I don't lose all of my emotional edge before I confront him. I really want to give him hell when I see him. You see – mental illness can be good for certain things. I need all the strength that psychosis can provide. It has to work at full speed to invent expressions that I can unleash on Michael someday. Who said that revenge can't be therapeutic?

I became aware of two more events. The mental health program located within the primary care center has been closed since the death of *Super*. My mother, the 'bitch of the West Side,' as I call her now – honoring *Super's* theories on 'Westsiders' masturbations on their intellectual superiority' – withdrew all funding for the therapy program to punish Joe for not taking care of me as he promised. She also convinced city and state governmental agencies that funded the mental health clinic to remove all funding. She explained that *Super's* death proved Joe's negligence. In short, she completely ruined a necessary and well-run service for the East Harlem community.

I told you – she is a bitch!

I feel that my inexperience and arrogance screwed up a whole community of around 200,000 people in the middle of Manhattan in just two weeks. Nobody knows where Joe is living now. He disappeared after all the funding stopped. The mental health program staff lives in the community, and many of them are still looking for work.

One Saturday afternoon – after a whole year – I had the courage to go back to the office. I still had the keys. I entered through the primary care clinic as I used to. I needed to force myself to revisit the experience of being there, and to make peace with that past reality. I had tried to do it earlier and failed.

After I entered the building, I went straight to my office. To my surprise, I saw my diploma still hanging on the wall; my desk and the chair that *Super* hated were still there. The first thing I did was to kick the hell out of that chair. Then I sat down on it, and I cried myself to sleep and dreamed. I dreamed that *Super* showed up in the office and spoke to me. "Hey! Wake up. Wake up!"

I answered, "What happened? You are here! What are you doing here?"

"I came to see you. Remember, we were supposed to meet one more time," he said.

"But you died."

"Yes, I did. I am glad that you are writing. You were so afraid that you even censored your own silence."

"But this is impossible," I said it, like a question.

"You can't see the enormity of the universe with your eyes open. You can only see it with your eyes closed. So, let's talk, *Columbia*."

"After a whole year, now you come to me?" I asked.

"It's not a good idea to try to stop time, *Columbia*. It's not time that passes – it is us!"

I responded furiously, "Now I know how ghosts commit suicide – they jump from mountains. I have bad news for you. Your suicide changed nothing! This world is as fucked up as when you left it. Why did you do it?"

"I didn't do it to change anything. I told you that I did it for myself. You own your death when you have owned your life. I earned every second of my death – I earned the right to say when. Please accept that, and you will feel better."

"What about your family?" I said.

"My daughter is great. It was tough, but now she has her own family. That's what counts."

"Your wife?"

"She loves me more now than when I was alive. She misses me and prays for me every night. She is not happy in her marriage. She wanted to come back to me, but she was too embarrassed to face me."

I was even frustrated with his ghost, "You see! Couldn't you fucking wait? Wait a little longer?"

"I wouldn't have returned to her. By the end of our sessions I had realized that it wouldn't have worked, even if I forgave her."

"So, what the fuck do you think now that you are dead?"

"My suicide was ironic," he said without sarcasm.

"Ironic?" I said. "Why ironic?'

"Before I jumped, I yelled, 'GOD, GO TO HELL!' – and then I went to live with him."

I was surprised. "Funny guy! Did you really find God?"

"Not yet," said *Super*. "I'm still in orientation."

"OK, I will go along with this orientation crap. What have you learned?"

"God can't force anyone to love. God doesn't do miracles. We are the ones who are supposed to do miracles, but we don't know it yet. God needs us more than we need God. Can you believe that? God needs us. I'm surprised God hasn't committed suicide yet."

"Stop joking," I said. "What are we then?"

"We are God's glitches. We are God's broken toys!"

"What is the meaning of life?" I asked.

"I still don't know. All I know is that we have many lives in one. Every second that passes is a different me. Thoughts are exhales, and each exhale is a farewell."

At that moment, I got up and hugged him. I said, "I thought we were going to be friends forever!"

"Well, kill yourself, and we can hang out!"

I yelled at him, "STOP TRYING TO BE FUNNY!"

"You will accept death better if you realize that many people feel suicidal from a death that happens to them before they die. On both sides of life and death, people want to escape their realities. You won't be alone."

"How do you know?" I asked.

"People are coming into your life that will need your help to create justice."

"What does that mean?" I said, confused.

"You will know sooner than you think."

"Am I doing the right thing?"

"There are no rights or wrongs in life. Only choices. Everything is a choice. We are guessing all the time, the best way we can. Whatever choice you make in life is always correct. I have to go now," he said.

"Don't go yet! – I must know something. – Please don't go yet! – Please!" I begged.

"Bye, my dear *Columbia.*"

"*SUPER!*" I yelled, and then whispered, "*Super!*"

I woke up, looked around, and I took my diploma from the wall and put it in my bag. I walked towards the door. I turned back before leaving for a last look at the seat where *Super* used to sit.

I turned around and opened the door to leave. Standing on the other side of the door there was a young Latina woman with a small girl who was holding her hand. I asked her, "How can I help you?"

She responded, "I have been looking for you for a while. I'm an attorney from California who especially wants to meet you."

I asked the woman, "And you are?"

"I'm Vidal Estrella's daughter. The *Super's* daughter Margarita, and this is my daughter Lucy. We want to know what happened…

I asked, "Do you have time for coffee? I have a story to tell you."

"I have all the time in the world," she said.

"Let's go." I closed the door and turned off the lights.

When someone dear dies, the last thing you want to do is remember... but remember you will.

## ABOUT THE AUTHOR

Jaime Antonio Estades was a Revson Fellow at Columbia University and received his Juris Doctor from the City University of New York School of Law, and his Master's in Social Work – from the Hunter College Silberman Graduate School of Social Work. Jaime continues to inspire the next generation of community activists, as an Adjunct Professor teaching Social Welfare Policy at Rutgers University Graduate School of Social Work and Social Policy, Advocacy, and Law and Social Work at both NYU and Columbia Graduate Schools of Social Work.

Jaime has committed his life to advocacy, education, health and leadership training. For the past 35 years, he has been working on issues relating to education, immigration, housing, voting rights and registration and family entitlement issues. Estades is the Executive Producer of the documentary "Let My People Vote," which chronicles the 2016 Presidential election in Orlando, Florida.

Jaime wrote the play "Five Sessions" that illustrates the racial and class tension in sessions of therapy. The play is currently being used in various universities, including Columbia University, to train clinical Social Work students.

In 1996, Jaime founded the Latino Leadership Institute, Inc. (LLI) where he still presides as Executive Director. LLI, a nonpartisan not-for-profit corporation, has trained hundreds of individuals on the fundamentals of campaign management and public policy through academies attended at no cost to participants, has hosted numerous colloquia, and sponsored civic engagement projects for high school students. In October 2015, the

Latino Leadership Institute was selected by the White House as one of the *Bright Spots of Excellence in Education in the Hispanic Community in the United States*. In 2016, LLI initiated a Chapter in Orlando, Florida, with two students elected to public office in the fall election cycle.

Jaime has also used his expertise to bolster the work of key non-profits, including the Boriken Neighborhood Health Center's development of the first eco-friendly (Green) Health Center in East Harlem. Jaime organized 250 families against the Los Sures Development Company, one of the worst landlords in Brooklyn. As Director for Advocacy for the Alliance for Quality Education, Jaime built, managed and coordinated coalitions of sixty community-based educational and labor organizations to improve the quality of public education in New York City. In 1996, during the Presidential election, as Executive Director of the Hispanic Education and Legal Fund, Jaime spearheaded the nonpartisan registration of over 100,000 new voters in New York, New Jersey, Pennsylvania, Massachusetts, Connecticut, Ohio, North Carolina and Florida.